The *Sisters' Story*

SAINT MARYS HOSPITAL – MAYO CLINIC
1889 TO 1939

The Sisters' Story

SAINT MARYS HOSPITAL – MAYO CLINIC
1889 TO 1939

Sister Ellen Whelan, O.S.F.

Mayo Foundation for Medical Education and Research
Rochester, Minnesota 55905

Printed in the United States of America

5 4 3 2 1

Library of Congress Control Number: 2002104585

ISBN 1-893005-93-3

TABLE OF CONTENTS

FOREWORD

In the beginning of the Sisters' Story, there were three physicians named Mayo who had a medical practice in Rochester and a group of Franciscan teaching Sisters open to serve the immediate needs of others according to the events of the times and the requests of their leaders. School was out for the summer, and these magnanimous women were available to help care for wounded, scared, and confused persons after a tornado struck Rochester in August 1883. Later, as Saint Marys Hospital was built and the Franciscan congregation served in both schools and the hospital, the teaching Sisters were regularly assigned as summer help at the hospital. An early need became a valued tradition.

When we, the Franciscan Sisters in the Rochester community, remember the stories of our early women at Saint Marys Hospital, we are very proud. Their long work days, which included doing the laundry for the hospital, cooking meals for patients, tending the gardens, learning about nursing so they could work in the surgery suite or in the general hospital wards, using individual gifts for administration, and trusting in the power of prayer, are inspirational. They believed that their work was of God.

In *The Sisters' Story*, the 50 years between 1889 and 1939 come alive with the challenges, successes, and nuances of relationships between the vigorous and competent women of the Sisters of Saint Francis and dedicated professional men and women, particularly the Doctors Mayo, who were determined to serve a health care need in southern Minnesota. This partnership, forged in a crisis, worked because Mother Alfred Moes and Dr. William Worrall Mayo respected the genius and dedication of each other. Each knew that the other was absolutely necessary in order to build and staff a quality hospital in Rochester. Mother Alfred is quoted in this very readable book as saying "you [Dr. W. W. Mayo] just promise me to take charge of it and we will set that building before you at once. With our faith and hope and energy, it will succeed." It did and has.

Author Ellen Whelan, O.S.F., combines factual research, anecdotal data, a bit of Irish wit, and a foundation of spirituality and values learned from her own life as a contemporary Rochester Franciscan professional woman to tell the stories of the Franciscan women who lived simply and ministered with compassion at Saint Marys Hospital from 1889 to 1939. Sister Ellen writes about the cultural context of the world and Rochester in the late 1800s and early 1900s. She includes family heritage stories of the Mayos and the Sisters. Links between personalities and snapshots of historical events help the reader understand the complex and unusual but remarkable collaborative relationships that are a part of the Sisters' Story at Saint Marys Hospital and Mayo Clinic.

Only a few Sisters of Saint Francis remain on the staff at Saint Marys Hospital. These competent and generous women carry forward the traditions of earlier times. However, the partnership that began more than 100 years ago with Dr. W. W. Mayo and Mother Alfred Moes was formalized in a new way in 1986 when Saint Marys Hospital was purchased by Mayo Foundation. The secular-religious connections that drew suspicion and derision from the general population and persons opposed to the collaborative venture in the early days have been smoothed by history and effort. What remains is a very workable challenge. The values that the Doctors Mayo and the Sisters of Saint Francis shared are still held in common and continue to influence daily practice and the ethics of decision making. Although the Sisters have no corporate role at Saint Marys Hospital, it is clear that there is a place for Franciscan influence and wisdom. This input is invited through regular Sponsorship Values Reviews, which ask health care providers and staff to reflect on similar Franciscan and Mayo values in their patient care, respect for colleagues, excellence of practice, and attention to the spiritual needs of patients and caregivers.

It is important to us, the Sisters of Saint Francis of the present generation, to direct passionate energy toward stewarding the legacy of the women who imagined and helped realize a facility for excellent health care delivered collaboratively in Rochester, Minnesota. To be a part of medical service to "anyone without regard to financial status, race, color, or creed" is still a mission for the Sisters of Saint Francis. The Sisters' Story from 1889 to 1939 is only the beginning of a story being written every day at Saint Marys Hospital and Mayo Clinic by women and men of distinction in their professional and personal lives.

Dolore Rockers, O.S.F.
President, Sisters of Saint Francis
Rochester, Minnesota

FOREWORD

"By [their] unceasing toil, by determination to make good, by willingness to offer whatever sacrifice the task demanded." These were the words used by the Mayo brothers about the founding Sisters of Saint Francis in Rochester. They explain the remarkable success and growth of Saint Marys Hospital. But the story of Saint Marys Hospital and the women whose mission was to relieve the suffering of humanity is more than a collection of historical facts and vignettes. Indeed, it is an inspiring example of how the shared vision of Mother Alfred Moes and the Sisters who worked with her in Rochester, together with the Doctors Mayo, created the world's most recognized and respected medical institution.

There can be little doubt that the Mayos were gifted and dedicated physicians, who by Mother Alfred's own assessment were the very best in Rochester and the region. It was a unique time, full of opportunity because relevant discoveries in medicine, especially anesthesia and antisepsis, made the science of surgery a practical and dependable means to cure illness and restore health. The full benefit of these promising advances, however, could not be realized in the office setting of the Doctors Mayo. Their surgical skills required the support of a modern inpatient facility.

Undoubtedly, the establishment of Saint Marys Hospital and the dedicated staffing by the Sisters of Saint Francis were key factors not only in enhancing the Mayo brothers' reputation and bringing Mayo Clinic to its current prominence in health care worldwide but also in advancing the science of medicine well beyond the confines of Minnesota. Mother Alfred clearly was the indefatigable force that led to the building of Saint Marys Hospital and the keystone in forging the essential partnership of the growing Mayo-led physician practice and the state-of-the-art hospital. We can only speculate what role Mayo Clinic would have in the world today if Dr. William Worrall Mayo's initial response had prevailed when he said, "Mother Superior, this city is too small to support a hospital."

From the earliest days to the present, Saint Marys Hospital and Mayo Clinic have been indivisible. It is remarkable that the key pioneers of both institutions—Sister Joseph Dempsey, Dr. Charles H. Mayo, and Dr. William J. Mayo—all departed the earth within months of each other in the same year. Nonetheless, the institutions they built have continued to enjoy phenomenal success, and the value they held dear—"The needs of the patient come first"—has remained constant.

As a Mayo Clinic physician, I will always be grateful for the individual and collective contributions of countless members of the Rochester Franciscan community, whose accomplishments come alive in *The Sisters' Story*.

Michael B. Wood, M.D.
President and Chief Executive Officer
    Mayo Foundation
Consultant, Division of Hand Surgery
    Mayo Clinic
Professor of Orthopedics
    Mayo Medical School

FOREWORD

The dates of this account of *The Sisters' Story* span a time long before the history of Saint Marys Hospital and Mayo Clinic had meaning to me. I trained at Mayo Clinic from 1967 to 1970, at which time I joined the Mayo Clinic staff in Diagnostic Radiology; consequently, my perspective is based on my experiences during the past 35 years as a physician, administrator, and member of the Saint Marys Sponsorship Board.

In medicine, we often think about origins and events, the workings of organizations, space and bricks and mortar, and what and why, and these are important considerations. *The Sisters' Story* is a wonderful account of all of these from 1889 to 1939. But the story goes deeper, to the culture, the personalities, the character, and the very soul of two organizations and the spirit of the Franciscan Sisters. Ellen Whelan, O.S.F., has managed to breathe life into the account of the Sisters who walked the halls of Saint Marys Hospital, cared for the sick, and touched the lives of Franciscan and Mayo leaders at the time and in later years.

The essence of the Sisters and Saint Marys Hospital is intertwined with the essence of the Doctors Mayo and Mayo Clinic. All were pioneers and innovators, dedicated, strong-willed yet self-sacrificing, and visionary. They focused intensely on the patients' needs, both physical and spiritual. The Sisters and Doctors Mayo were fiercely independent in their views and there were contentious issues. They were also fiercely interdependent and focused on the success of both Saint Marys Hospital and Mayo Clinic. Despite the diversity of their backgrounds, they shared common goals and objectives: to provide the best patient care supported by education and research. Clinical research in surgical technique and instruments, operating room procedures, and dietetics and the education of young physicians and nurses were integral parts of their mission. From the beginning, they saw beyond patient care designed for the community to a multispecialty medical and surgical practice that reached national and international levels. In the early years the cultures were compatible, and in the later years each culture was influenced and shaped by the other. Both the Sisters and the Doctors Mayo made the confident decision that they could rely on one another.

The working relationship between the Mayos and the Sisters was based on a handshake. That trust has continued during my career on the staff of Mayo Clinic. Mayo Clinic physicians and scientists are appointed not by a contract but by a handshake, which, in Mayo culture, is a stronger bond.

The history, the personalities, the dedication, the focus on the value that "the needs of the patient come first," and the shared respect and trust were the underpinnings that allowed the merger of assets and leadership of Saint Marys Hospital and Mayo Foundation in 1986. This merger of a Catholic hospital and a secular clinic is a unique model in health care. The partnership of the Sisters and the Doctors Mayo and their organizations did not dissipate with the deaths of Dr. William J. Mayo, Dr. Charles H. Mayo, and Sister Joseph Dempsey in 1939. My colleagues on the staff of Mayo Clinic and the Sisters I have known have sustained the bond that connects them. The spirit of the Sisters today is personified by Sister Generose Gervais, who is emeritus administrator of Saint Marys Hospital and president of the Poverello Foundation and as well known for her leadership and dedication as for her pickles and jams and jellies. Since 1986, the Board of Governors of Mayo Clinic in Rochester and the Saint Marys Hospital Sponsorship Board enjoy and share the same focus on the needs of the patient that the Franciscan Sisters and the Doctors Mayo did in the course of their history.

Why *The Sisters' Story* now? This book will give the staffs of Saint Marys Hospital and Mayo Clinic a deeper understanding of the culture and legacy of their past, better enabling them to see and to seize the opportunities to care for the sick with compassion and to nurture the physical and the spiritual needs in the unique Mayo Clinic model of patient care. Sculptures of Mother Alfred Moes and of the Mayo brothers are being created and will be placed with a statue of Dr. William Worrall Mayo on the grounds of the Mayo Building and newly dedicated Gonda Building. These pioneers in medical care worked and planned together in the early years. Now they will be reminders of that history and culture in the years to come.

Robert R. Hattery, M.D.
Consultant, Department of Radiology
Mayo Clinic
Professor of Radiology
Mayo Medical School
Rochester, Minnesota

ACKNOWLEDGMENTS

Behind *The Sisters' Story* is another story, a chronicle of persons, groups, and institutions whose generosity made the book a reality. My religious congregation, the Sisters of Saint Francis of Rochester, Minnesota, asked me to write the book and supported the project with prayers, friendship, and financial resources. The Sisters of Saint Marys Hospital, past and present, inspired the book with their extraordinary spirit and selfless dedication. I am grateful to governance group members, Sisters Colleen Byron, Gavin Hagan, Jean Keniry, Joanne Loecher, Marlene Pinzka, and Katarina Schuth. Sister Generose Gervais offered professional expertise, seasoned wisdom, and sisterly care throughout the project.

The Saint Marys Hospital Sponsorship Board endorsed the book from its beginnings; Jerry Mahoney and Jeanne Klein continue to provide generous assistance. Saint Marys Hospital Auxiliary/Volunteers, who funded the cost of publication, also supported the project in many other ways. Departments and individuals across Mayo Clinic shared expertise and resources far beyond my expectations. For example, the Division of Systems & Procedures provided office space and services for an extended time. Following are names of some of the individuals: Dick Hines, Craig Smoldt, Jean Keane, Claire Bender, Robert Blomberg, Pat McConnell, Molly McMahon, Anne Purrington, Pearlene Long, and Steve Kopecky.

Research for the book took many forms, including extensive personal interviews. Saint Marys Hospital archivist, Sister Lauren Weinandt, who first conceived the idea of a book on the Sisters of Saint Marys Hospital, offered invaluable help. Besides contributing resource material on a regular basis, she augmented the written word with wonderful stories. Sister Mary Lonan Reilly shared key information from the archives of the Sisters of Saint Francis. Mona Stevermer and the staff of Saint Marys Hospital Library offered unfailing help throughout the process. Carolyn Beck provided an important perspective on information from the Mayo Clinic archives. The Rochester Public Library and Olmsted County History Center were excellent resources of information and professional assistance.

Writing a book for the first time was a challenge, and I was fortunate to have gifted readers. Chapter by chapter, they provided helpful criticism and encouragement. My deepest thanks to David Leonard, Judith Thistle, Tony Wiggins, and Sisters Marlene Pinzka, Eileen Haugh, Cashel Weiler, and Katarina Schuth.

For their expertise in publishing the book, I am grateful to the Mayo Clinic Section of Scientific Publications and my editor, LeAnn Stee, for friendship and assistance. My thanks, also, to Roberta Schwartz and the excellent production group composed of Kenna Atherton, Mary Ayshford, Jon Bedsted, Virginia Dunt, Jeff Satre, and Ron Ward.

Promotion and distribution of the book were new challenges; again, able volunteers contributed time and talent in the persons of Kay Batchelder, Dorothy Haley, Phyllis Hosking, Karen Ostrander, Pauline Walle, and Judy Wilder. My thanks also to Mayo Clinic professionals who unstintingly assisted our efforts: Suzanne Leaf-Brock in Communications and Rebecca Roberts and James Hale in Mayo Medical Ventures.

Finally, thanks to my family—one and all—from nephew Kevin and his wife Kate whose interest and encouragement cheered me on to my brother Mike, who is sure *The Sisters' Story* will be a major motion picture (he wants to play Dr. Charlie). To them and to all those mentioned, directly or indirectly, I offer thanks not only for their help but also for their unfailing reminder that it is indeed more blessed to give than to receive.

Sister Ellen Whelan, O.S.F
July 1, 2002

CHAPTER 1

Roads to Rochester

The Sisters' Story of Saint Marys Hospital begins like many good stories. Once upon a time, a group of Catholic Sisters and a family of physicians built a hospital in a cornfield. The hospital has grown to become a place of healing for people from all over the world. The miracle in a cornfield had its origin in events as large as the American frontier movement and as small as the accidents of personal relationships. This chapter describes the beginning events and relationships that helped create Saint Marys Hospital. As a cornerstone, they offer keys for understanding the foundations of this story—once upon a time and today.

In the spring of 1864, when Abraham Lincoln was president, an immigrant railroad laborer named Patrick Dempsey waited in Buffalo, New York, for the morning train to take him and his family to Minnesota. Next to him, his wife, Mary Sullivan Dempsey, held their baby, Helen. Daughters Catherine and Julia looked after younger siblings Dennis and Mary nearby. The Dempseys had decided to stake their future on new land in the unseen, unfamiliar Minnesota frontier.

Julia, the Dempsey's second child, 8 years old, was small for her age and had bright brown eyes. As an adult, Julia would become Sister Joseph, one of the founding Franciscan Sisters of Saint Marys Hospital and hospital administrator for almost 50 years. Julia's parents were Catholic immigrants from Ireland who came to the United States to escape starvation, disease, and persecution. Her family history made a marked impact on Julia personally and on her life choices.

Just as Julia traveled to a new home in a new land, some 10 years earlier her parents had sailed across the Atlantic Ocean to the United States in search of a new home. Their first 10 years in their new country brought Patrick and Mary to adulthood with marriage and family responsibilities. These were years of adjustment in which they found a fit for themselves as immigrant pioneers. Such life experiences, in combination with time and distance, helped heal the harsh memories of the life they had left behind in Ireland.

Patrick and Mary were part of the large migration of Irish who came to the United States in the wake of the Potato Famine that began in 1846 and within 4 years completely ravaged Ireland. The roots of famine went back several centuries to the British conquest of Ireland. The Irish, relegated to live in rural areas on small plots of land, farmed these plots for food and grew the potato because of its high yield and nutritive value. They were dependent on the potato "not as a staple, but as the exclusive component of their diet. . . ."

Sister Mary Joseph Dempsey as a young girl of 14 years. (From Saint Marys Hospital Archives.)

The Irish had experienced crop reversal before; "indeed, a government commission estimated that one-third of the population lived in semi-starvation *every summer* before the new crop [of potatoes] came in. . . ." The crop failures of the 1840s, however, were of unprecedented proportion. In the midst of pervasive hunger, typhus quickly followed and became a raging pestilence. As many as a million people died of starvation and disease in a country of 8.5 million.

Faced with these oppressive conditions, the Irish left their country in large numbers and many never wanted to return. Their memories were painful—starving children in Kilkenny "mysteriously gone bald and whiskered, so that they looked like monkeys or aged dwarfs"; hordes of men, women, and children crowded onto roads joining hundreds of others going from place to place in search of food. They died in the ditches, and bodies of the dead were left in the hedgerows because there were too many for the living to bury. Easily 2 million people left Ireland on "coffin ships," where thousands would perish. Of those who survived, 75% came to the United States. Patrick and Mary Dempsey were among them.

The 1855 U.S. census for the town of Bucktooth, later named Salamanca, in Cattaraugus County, New York, records the Dempseys living in a log house valued at $3.00. Patrick Dempsey is described as 31, an Irish-born alien with no occupation, who "cannot read or write." Mary Dempsey is listed as 25, born in Ireland. They had one daughter, Catherine, 4 years old. A boarder, Patrick Sullivan, probably Mary's brother, lived with them.

Five years later, the 1860 census shows the Dempseys with four children, three boarders, and a new home. Patrick, no longer described as alien, is a railroad laborer. They no longer lived in a log house. Their home was frame and presumably larger to accommodate three more children and two extra boarders. The Dempseys, who left a country of little opportunity and great despair, had begun to make a new life for themselves in the United States. Much of Ireland's despair and lack of opportunity were related to religion. Generations of Irish were Roman Catholic. When the Protestant armies of Oliver Cromwell conquered Ireland in 1695, the Irish became a subjugated people. Those who chose to remain Catholic lost most of their rights, including the rights to vote and hold office, to own property beyond a certain value, to attend university, and to worship. For the Protestant British, discrimination on the basis of religion was clearly justified. They believed that the Roman Catholic Church was the mainstay of Irish nationalism and at the root of Irish rebellion against British rule. They also feared any collusion of the Irish with rival Catholic powers such as France or Spain. The penal laws against Catholics maintained British ascendancy in Ireland and diminished possible threats to the British Empire abroad.

Persecution served to strengthen the role of the church in the life of the Irish people. Its corporate existence, directed from Rome, made it the only institution to persist unchanged through terrors, misery, and defeat. Catholic philosophy and theology provided an intellectual foundation. Sacraments and rituals gave meaning to suffering. The Catholic faith that Mary and Patrick Dempsey grew up with in Ireland continued to be an essential part of their lives in the United States. From earliest childhood, Julia Dempsey and her siblings heard stories about their faith from their parents. They learned how to pray largely by observing their parents pray. The children looked to Jesus, Mary, and the saints, much as they looked to their parents, for nourishment, guidance, and solace.

Catholic worship, prayers, and customs were part of Irish daily life, and parish priests played a significant role in major life decisions. The Irish considered them natural protectors and trusted leaders. During the long years of persecution, Catholic priests proved worthy of trust, mainstays who bolstered the Irish in their daily lives. When the Dempseys heard that priests in western New York State offered help to Irish immigrants, they settled first in that area. In a similar way, the advice of the clergy was important in the Dempseys' subsequent decision to move west to Minnesota. Minnesota church leaders who worked to bring Catholics to the frontier focused on the immigrant Irish arriving by the thousands in the 1850s. L. P. Cotter, father of the first bishop of Winona, wrote often in the Boston *Pilot*, urging his countrymen to leave

Rochester, Minnesota, 1864.

the overcrowded cities of the east for new opportunities in Minnesota: ". . . many a goodly quarter section lies waiting for the plowshare and the hands of some honest Celtic farmer. . . . Throw off . . . servitude, . . . take up the 'Westward march,' become tillers of the soil . . . spread religion and civilization hand in hand."

Father John Ireland, the son of Irish immigrants, wanted Catholics to become a vital part of the American experience. Assimilation was most possible, he argued, for Catholics who settled the frontier and became part of building a civic community. Under Ireland's leadership, the church in Minnesota organized the Minnesota Irish Emigrant Society in 1864. Newsletters were bulletin boards for the frontier; they told readers how to get to Minnesota, what to pack, and how much money to bring. Eight years after founding the Society, Father Ireland addressed the members and spoke about "the great amount of good accruing to those who have acted upon our advice. . . . We can point, thank God, this day to hundreds and thousands of our countrymen, now settled, and in a fair way to prosperity and happiness, who a few years ago were living from hand to mouth; and who, a few years ago, were scarcely the owners of the chairs they sat on, and who to-day can rest themselves under their own vine and fig trees, the owners of broad and fertile acres."

Despite such efforts, three-fourths of Irish immigrants opted to stay in the cities of the East and Northeast. They chose menial urban jobs and tried to duplicate the village life they had left behind. Immigrant Irish distrusted the American Protestant establishment and preferred to stay with their own people in the cities. As one scholar put it, their limited experience with farming was living in grinding poverty on small plots controlled by an exploitative land system. Surviving the famine and the Atlantic crossing had, for many, used up most of their energy and initiative. They were content to become "pioneers of the American urban ghettos."

The Dempseys, who followed Father Ireland's advice, were among the minority of Irish who chose to move to the western frontier. They set aside fears and grudges of the past to better spend their energies on the present. For Julia Dempsey, later Sister Joseph, her parents' example had an important influence. During her long tenure as administrator of Saint Marys Hospital, Sister Joseph characteristically showed openness and goodwill to persons of every race, nationality, and religion.

A strong attraction for the Dempseys was free land; the Homestead Act of 1862 promised settlers 160 acres of frontier land for the taking. Also, they had relatives living near Rochester, Minnesota, who encouraged Patrick and Mary to join them. The entire trip from Buffalo, New York, to Rochester, took about 10 days, and railroads were available for a good share of the journey. The New York Central went as far as Chicago, and from there the Chicago Rock Island went to the port of Galena, Illinois, on the Mississippi River. At Galena, they boarded one of the daily steamboats, going as far as LaCrosse, Wisconsin. In LaCrosse, they joined a group of covered wagons that followed the Dubuque

Father John Ireland, 1862. He later became archbishop of Minneapolis and St. Paul, Minnesota. (From O'Connell MR: John Ireland and the American Catholic Church. St. Paul, MN: Minnesota Historical Society Press, 1988, p 67. By permission of the Minnesota Historical Society.)

Trail, which went through Rochester on the way to St. Paul, Minnesota.

When the Dempseys arrived in Rochester in 1864, they found a bustling city of 3,000. The downtown flourished with offices, stores, and a new First National Bank. Rochester had two newspapers, eight hotels, two breweries, seven saloons, one billiard parlor, and several dozen stores. Newcomers were impressed with the courthouse and the Calvary Episcopal Church built just across the road. Rochester's location at the heart of a system of river valleys made it a natural center, and settlers had arrived as early as 1854. The caravans of covered wagons that rolled into town predicted a positive future, and Rochester became the seat of Olmsted County.

The Dempseys headed east out of Rochester toward the rolling hills of Haverhill Township. Their destination was a section called "Irish Ridge." Other Irish families had settled the Ridge as early as 1858, when Minnesota became the 32nd state. These families warmly welcomed the Dempseys and helped Patrick plant his first crop of wheat. In 1864, wheat yields and wheat prices brought new prosperity to the area. Productive soil, the demand for wheat, and competition among buyers made profits high. Farmers lined up on roads with wagons heaped high waiting to dump their loads into elevator hoppers. "Wheat buyers, many of them agents for dealers in Milwaukee and Chicago, gathered at every entrance to town and as the wagons passed them called out their bids." Competition among them raised

Rochester skyline.

the price and the farmers' profits. Farmers' wives and daughters who came along "to do a little trading" crowded the streets and stores. Wheat buyers and speculators helped fill the hotels and saloons, sometimes to overflowing. The annual county fair brought crowds so in excess of the available accommodations that visitors slept on straw in the local churches and paid 50¢ for the privilege. State conventions met in the thriving city along with fraternal orders, schoolteachers, church leaders, temperance enthusiasts, and spiritualists. Citizens of Rochester exuded confidence in themselves and optimism about the future of their city and region. Although most were new to Minnesota, they were not new to the United States. Rochester's founding citizens were members of European families whose ancestors had resided in North America for several generations. Called Old Stock Americans, they were the host society of the United States with a culture based on British law and the Protestant work ethic. Rochester's healthy climate and good economic opportunity prompted them to come to Minnesota.

William Worrall Mayo, a central person in the Sisters' Story, came to Rochester in 1863. Like the Old Stock Americans, he valued Rochester's healthy climate and economically thriving community. At first glance, Mayo appeared similar in most respects to his host society. His background was English and Protestant; he was middle-class and educated. A closer examination of his background, however, suggests important differences between him and many of his Rochester neighbors. Born near Manchester in 1819, William W. Mayo grew up in England's industrial north during the early Industrial Revolution. Manchester was fired with social and political unrest. Laborers gathered outside the city in St. Peter's Field in 1819 and demonstrated for economic rights and parliamentary reform. Magistrates sent mounted troops who charged the unarmed crowd. Without warning they fired on the people, killing some and wounding others. The people called it the "Peterloo Massacre." In 1826, when William was 7 years old, his father died. That same year, 90,000 unemployed weavers and spinners smashed machines and burned factories in Manchester. When their food ran out, they stormed bakeries and shops. William's family was middle-class and gave him a good education, but his home in the industrial north did not provide "the right side of the tracks environment." Biographer Helen Clapesattle asks about the influence these formative years had on him: "Did it plant in him the seeds of a social and political conscience, nurture an inclination to champion the economic underdog, and set growing a firm conviction that government must be for *all* the people? No direct evidence supports an affirmative answer, but in his maturity William W. Mayo possessed those characteristics in full flower."

William W. Mayo came from a family whose ancestors had distinguished themselves as physicians. Although he did not earn a medical degree during his years in England, he studied chemistry and later medicine for a time in Manchester, London, and Glasgow. The famous scientist John Dalton, who tutored young William in chemistry, was an important influence. Oxford and Cambridge considered John Dalton unorthodox for his Quaker beliefs and did not invite him to join their universities. Nevertheless, he became the father of atomic theory and founder of the periodic table. Dalton was a person of quiet demeanor and simple habits who taught his students through the empirical method. Under his guidance, students learned by doing experiments and testing results. Dalton's method of teaching encouraged William to look for meanings and connections beyond the surface of things. Much of the practical chemistry Dalton taught William was pharmaceutical in nature, the type of knowledge that would stand him in good stead when he decided to explore a broader world.

The United States offered opportunity of every kind and prompted William to set off for the country in 1845, when he was 25 years old. He left without family permission and good-byes, but not because of any ill feeling; this was just his impetuous way. William W. Mayo had the look of independence about him. Short and slight, only 5 feet 4 inches tall, he held his head high, his back straight. The piercing glance of his blue-gray eyes registered decisive self-assurance.

William had no trouble finding work when he arrived in New York City. His first position was at Bellevue Hospital, which served as a charity hospital, a municipal almshouse, and an insane asylum. In all likelihood William worked as a pharmacist in the drug department. Bellevue at that time was "at its nadir of neglect and political exploitation." Politicians appointed the medical staff, and shortly before William arrived prisoners served as the nursing staff. When the prisoners left, derelicts replaced them as nurses and continued a tradition of rough, unsympathetic care of the sick. Food was insufficient, fuel was inadequate, and bed linen went unwashed. Infectious diseases were rife, and medical staff and patients alike suffered from them. In 1847, 10 of the 13 assistant physicians died of typhus. That year, William W. Mayo left Bellevue Hospital and New York; he had seen enough. Mayo's experience at Bellevue Hospital probably underlined his negative attitude toward hospitals; years later, he expressed such views when a Franciscan

Sister asked for his help in building a hospital for Rochester.

From New York City, William went west to Buffalo, New York, and by canal to Lafayette, Indiana, on the banks of the Wabash River. In Lafayette, he met a leading physician, Elizur H. Deming, M.D., who, in addition to his medical credentials, had a strong academic background from Williams College. Encouraged by Dr. Deming to resume his medical studies, William enrolled in the Indiana Medical College at La Porte, about 50 miles from Lafayette, for the 1849-1850 session. Dr. Deming was his preceptor.

When compared with an earlier period, medical school standards in the United States declined before the Civil War. Between 1810 and 1840, the U.S. population increased from 7 to 17 million. The fast-growing population demanded more physicians, and the number of medical schools increased rapidly. Twenty-six new schools opened during this period, most of them owned by physicians who gave lectures to medical students for a fee. Many of the new schools, however, had a short life. Badly planned and poorly staffed, they set no requirements for admission and gave no grades. Students received a diploma at the end of two lecture sessions of 5 or 6 months each. Regular attendance at lectures was not required, and examinations were generally cursory. Between the two lecture sessions, students were assigned a physician-preceptor. Many students, however, saw nothing of their preceptor from the time they registered as apprentices until they received their degrees. Ten or twelve months was the total time most physicians gave to their training. Advocates of medical reform pointed out that it took longer to learn the trade of a machinist, printer, or river boat pilot. No overriding authority existed to prevent abuses in medical education. Physicians who promoted reform received strong opposition from colleagues who owned proprietary schools. Physician-proprietors feared that upgraded require-ments and an improved curriculum would put their schools out of business.

At this stage of medical education, William W. Mayo became a physician. He received his medical degree on February 14, 1850. His year at the Indiana Medical College cost him $100 in fees and $50 for 16 weeks' board and room in La Porte.

After his graduation in 1850, Dr. Mayo went back to Lafayette and practiced medicine. A year later, his friends read in the newspaper about his marriage to Miss Louise Abigail Wright on February 2, 1851. Later, when his friends met the bride, they found her "a buxom young woman, slightly taller than her husband, with energy, determination, and intelligence quite equal to his." Louise Wright Mayo was born near Syracuse, New York. She

worked hard as a young girl doing domestic chores and had little opportunity for formal schooling. She was an avid reader, however, and everyone
who met her thought her an educated woman of keen intelligence. At 18
years old, Louise had gone alone by canal barge to live with relatives in
Michigan and later moved with them to La Porte. Louise and William met
in La Porte during the year he studied medicine at Indiana Medical College.
Soon after their marriage, Louise began her own business as a milliner.

Malaria was the great scourge of Lafayette and the Wabash Valley in the
mid-19th century. Sometimes physicians arrived at their patient's home so
weakened by alternating chills and fever that they had to lie down before
attending to the patient. Dr. Mayo himself fell victim to the disease. The
recurrence of the disease every summer was too much for him. "'Hell,' he
insisted, 'is a place where people have malaria.'" One summer day in 1854,
in the midst of a chill, he stomped into the barn, hitched up the horse and
buggy, and shouted to his startled wife as he drove west, "'Good-bye, Louise.
I'm going to keep on driving until I get well or die.'" Looking for a new
place to settle, he arrived in Galena, Illinois, on the Mississippi River, where
he heard boasts about the new Minnesota Territory: "there is no fever and
ague . . . not . . . one case of sickness in the whole of Hennepin County for
several weeks past."

Dr. Mayo caught one of the crowded daily steamboats to St. Paul in late
June or July 1854. When he stepped off the boat, he found the spirit of optimism almost palpable. Enthusiasm abounded for more settlers, larger crops,
and new businesses. Land values would rise, markets would expand, and
fortunes would be made. Whether it was this infectious enthusiasm, the
beauty of the country, or an improvement in his health, he never said, but
Dr. Mayo went back to Indiana and brought his wife and daughter Gertrude
to St. Paul. After settling in St. Paul, Louise resumed her millinery business. When Dr. Mayo assessed prospects for a medical practice, he found
the area had more than enough physicians. He accepted a surveyor's position in order to see something of Minnesota. In the fall of 1854, Dr. Mayo
made two trips alone on foot to Duluth, and the following January he went
again, this time with three other men. They wore snowshoes and arrived
in 6 days.

Within a short time Dr. Mayo gave up the idea of surveying for a living
and decided to find a new location that could support his medical practice.
He explored areas of Minnesota below St. Paul. Traveling south on the
Minnesota River, he came to a rich agricultural area west of the Mississippi

River. The village of Le Sueur particularly impressed him; in the spring of 1856, he moved his family to a farm in the area and a year later to the town itself. Dr. Mayo established his medical practice, but also took other jobs. The citizens of Le Sueur elected him justice of the peace. He worked as a veterinarian and published a newspaper. Seeing a need for a ferry across the Minnesota River, he started one and operated the ferry himself. Mayo piloted a steamboat at the same time that young James J. Hill, later the famous builder of railroad empires, served as accountant for one of the boats going up and down the Minnesota River. J. J. Hill and W. W. Mayo began a friendship in those years that lasted all their lives.

The Civil War erupted in 1861. Dr. Mayo volunteered as regimental surgeon for the Union, but he was not accepted. Two years later, he secured the examining surgeon position for the Union's enrollment board in the southern half of Minnesota. The board selected Rochester for its headquarters, and Dr. Mayo reported for duty in May 1863. Rochester's vitality as an economic regional center suited him. Within a few months, he purchased two lots on Third Avenue and built a small house on one of them. He moved his family to Rochester early in 1864.

Rochester citizens soon recognized Dr. Mayo as one of the area's most competent physicians. Although patients considered him a courteous and sympathetic confidant, he did not invite familiarity; no one called him "Bill" or "Will." He dressed his small frame in a long-tailed, double-breasted coat and wore a tall top hat. Dr. Mayo, it was said, "drove his horse and buggy like a madman." He had a special carriage designed with a belt so that he could strap himself to the seat in the event of an unexpected accident. His long buggy rides through the

William Worrall Mayo, M.D., country doctor.

countryside visiting patients provided time for reflection on matters small and large. Dr. Mayo thrived on new scientific ideas and looked for ways to apply them. Frequently his notes on patients concluded with the statement: "Left open for further thought and research." He found room for a laboratory near his office and was one of the first physicians to use the microscope regularly. Indeed, he mortgaged his home to pay for a new and improved model.

Dr. Mayo became active in Rochester civic affairs and conducted a successful campaign for a city library. With members of the library's executive committee, he selected the first 1,500 books and established a comfortable reading room above the new First National Bank. In 1867, Rochester citizens elected Dr. Mayo to the school board. About this time, the board decided to construct a new building. Within a year Rochester had "one of the finest school buildings in the West—a brick building, five stories, sixteen rooms, single desks, and furnace heat, cost $65,000." Dr. Mayo held strong opinions, which sometimes put him at odds with other Rochester leaders. His convictions about science and theology were particularly strong points of disagreement. The public followed with interest the growing conflict between science and religion. Charles Darwin's theory of evolution, interpreted by Thomas Huxley, was the focus of dispute. Dr. Mayo favored Darwin's theory that endorsed science as an intellectual discipline, and he believed it would free the world of misery and ignorance. He read Huxley's expositions aloud to his friends "and defended Darwin by the hour." Darwin's theory on evolution, however, challenged prevailing religious views, which held that all human life descended from Adam and Eve.

Dr. William Worrall Mayo's newspaper advertisement (top left) was characteristically straightforward.

Dr. Mayo's endorsement of evolution shocked citizens who took their Bible literally. Community leader John Edgar called Dr. Mayo "an infidel and friend of demon rum" and led a successful campaign to defeat him for reelection to the school board in 1870.

Although Edgar's characterization was flagrantly inaccurate, Dr. Mayo was unorthodox in religion and politics and proud of it. He said he never felt a need to belong to any formal religion: "My own religion has been to do all the good I could to my fellow men, and as little harm as possible." He respected faith practiced with sincerity by others, but for himself took churchgoing with a grain of salt. In politics, Dr. Mayo was a Democrat in a Republican county. One admirer recalled: "He was a democrat in principle and in politics, and believed that every man, woman, and child was entitled to a fair showing." Furthermore, he held that education, opportunity, and wealth carried an obligation to live with integrity and provide civic leadership. He believed that people given more of this world's goods should help others less fortunate. He refused to collect fees from patients who had few financial resources; his compassion for the weak and support for under-dogs were well known. Such strong social and political principles bear out biographer Helen Clapesattle's suggestion that Dr. Mayo's childhood experiences profoundly influenced his adult conscience.

By some standards, Dr. Mayo was also unorthodox in the company he kept. His friendship with young Thomas O'Gorman, the new pastor of St. John's Catholic Church, shocked some of the townspeople. At first glance, Father O'Gorman seemed an unusual colleague for Dr. Mayo by anyone's standards. This son of Irish immigrants, however, had an unusual back-ground, thanks to Joseph Cretin, the first bishop of St. Paul. Bishop Cretin chose Thomas O'Gorman and his childhood friend, John Ireland, as the first seminarians for his new diocese and sent them to study in France.

The 13 years that O'Gorman studied in France had a profound influence on him. His stringent spiritual formation became a norm of conduct for a life-time; learning history, language, and culture cultivated his intellectual capac-ities. In addition, the experience gave him the panache that he showed in the performance of a multitude of missionary duties on the frontier of Minnesota.

His first assignment as pastor in Rochester provided Father O'Gorman with many new experiences. Later, he recalled the significance of his friend-ship with Dr. W. W. Mayo. Differences in age and religious beliefs, which might have been an obstacle to friendship, seemed to enhance their rela-tionship. Both men were bookish, mutually curious about new ideas;

Father Thomas O'Gorman, second pastor of St. John's Catholic Church, Rochester, Minnesota. He later became bishop of Sioux Falls, South Dakota. (Courtesy of St. John's Catholic Church, Rochester, MN.)

St. John's Catholic Church, located on First Street and Second Avenue Southwest, was built in 1872. (Courtesy of St. John's Catholic Church, Rochester, MN.)

undoubtedly, they found each other interesting companions. The physician and the priest made house calls together, with Dr. Mayo as driver, "because he had the faster horses."

Father O'Gorman is important to the Sisters' Story of Saint Marys Hospital for providing an important link among several key persons. Because he was pastor to the Dempsey family, Sister Joseph knew him well, and Father John Ireland was his boyhood friend. O'Gorman's friendship with Sister Joseph, Dr. W. W. Mayo, and Father John Ireland disposed them to have a high regard and trust in each other. Further, it was Father Thomas O'Gorman who would persuade a group of religious Sisters to staff his parish school, and they, in turn, brought another important institution to Rochester.

ENDNOTES

Pages 1-6
Interviews with Sister Joseph Dempsey's nieces, Sister Carmela Dempsey, O.S.F., and Sister Marcellita Dempsey, O.S.F., are the major source of information on the Dempsey family history. These interviews, conducted at Assisi Heights, Rochester, MN, from 1998 to 2001, provided historical data on the Dempsey family as well as extensive information about Sister Joseph.

Page 2
O'Connell MR: *John Ireland and the American Catholic Church.* **St. Paul: Minnesota Historical Society Press, 1988, pp 10-12.**

Pages 2-3
Woodham-Smith C: *The Great Hunger: Ireland 1845-1849.* **New York: Old Town Books, 1962, pp 38-53, 206-238.**
This book provides a comprehensive account of the causes and effects of the Irish Famine.

McCaffrey LJ: *The Irish Diaspora in America.* **Bloomington: Indiana University Press, 1976, pp 11-29.**

Shannon WV: *The American Irish.* **New York: The Macmillan Company, 1966, p 6.**

Page 3
Interviews with Beverly Zoccali, librarian of the Salamanca Public Library, Salamanca, NY, and Lorna Spencer, curator of Cattaraugus County Memorial and Historical Museum, Little Valley, NY, provided background information on 19th century Irish settlements in the area. U.S. census records of 1855 and 1860 offered documentation on Patrick and Mary Dempsey and their children when they resided in Salamanca.

Page 4
Crozier W: *Gathering a People: A History of the Diocese of Winona.* **Winona, MN: Diocese of Winona, 1989, p 29.**
This book quotes at length from the November 8, 1856, letter of L. P. Cotter to the Boston *Pilot*, which promoted the new diocese of Winona among the Irish.

Pages 4-5
Ireland J: Address of the Irish Immigration Society for the Year 1872. In: *John Ireland Papers. Archives of the Archdiocese of Minneapolis and St. Paul, MN.*

Page 5   **O'Connell MR:** *John Ireland and the American Catholic Church*, **p 16.** O'Connell summarizes the reasons why so many of the Irish stayed in the cities of the East and Northeast.

Page 5   **McCaffrey LJ:** *The Irish Diaspora in America*, **pp 78-79.** McCaffrey contrasts Irish Catholics who remained in the northeast and those who moved farther west: "Massachusetts Irish Catholics lived in a highly-structured society dominated by a Protestant Ascendancy determined to retain power and the status quo. New England Irishmen started on the basement floor of the American class structure and tended to stay there. Their ghettos were loaded with failure and defeatism, producing a paranoid vision of religion, politics, and other Americans. . . . Newly-arrived Irish immigrants who stayed out of New England were more likely to do well in the United States than third or fourth-generation Boston Irishmen. In the Mid-Atlantic states and in the Midwest and West, they lived with and competed against Anglo-American Protestants and members of other ethnic groups, and the farther west the Irish went, the more confident and competitive they became."

Page 6   **Rucker CW:** *For the 110th Anniversary of the Unitarian-Universalist Church, November 21, 1976*, **p 1. (Mayo Historical Suite, Mayo Clinic, Rochester, MN.)**

       Hodgson HW: *Rochester: City of the Prairie.* **Windsor Publications, 1989, pp 9-21.**

       Raygor MW: *The Rochester Story.* **Rochester, MN: Schmidt Printing, 1976, pp 5-37.**

       The Dempseys' journey to Minnesota replicated that of most other settlers coming to the state at that time. These accounts provide an engaging picture of early Rochester.

Page 7   **Rice JG: The Old-Stock Americans. In:** *They Chose Minnesota: A Survey of the State's Ethnic Groups.* **Edited by Holmquist JD. St. Paul: Minnesota Historical Society Press, 1981.** Rice provides an interesting account of Old Stock Americans, their various origins and important influence.

       Clapesattle H: *The Doctors Mayo.* **Minneapolis: The University of Minnesota Press, 1941.** This is the definitive history of the Mayos. Clapesattle's prodigious work, from beginning to end, provided an invaluable resource for this writer.

Pages 6-7   **Clapesattle H:** *The Doctors Mayo,* **pp 87-88.**
             Clapesattle gives a spirited description of early Rochester.

Pages 7-8   **Clapesattle** describes William Worrall Mayo's early influences
             (pp 10-11).

Pages 7-8   **Clapesattle** quotation **(p 11).**

Pages 8-9   **Clapesattle (pp 11-24)** describes William W. Mayo's medical education
             within the context of British and American medical education at the
             time.

Page 9   **Bordley J III, Harvey AM:** *Two Centuries of American Medicine: 1776-*
             1976. **Philadelphia: W. B. Saunders Company, 1976, pp 20-29.**
             This text provides an overview of medical education in the United
             States, 1840-1870.

Pages 9-11   **Clapesattle** describes Louise Wright Mayo on **pages 25 and 26**; she
             recounts the great scourge of malaria in northern Indiana and Dr.
             Mayo's reaction on **pages 28 to 32.** Chapter Two, "On the Minnesota
             Frontier," **pages 33 to 65**, recounts the Mayo family's introduction to
             the Minnesota frontier, and Chapter Four, "Rochester Then," **pages
             87 to 107**, provides an excellent resource for Dr. William W. Mayo's
             first years in Rochester.

Page 13   **Toomey DP:** *W. W. Mayo Papers.* **Mayo Historical Suite, Mayo Clinic.**
             From an unpublished paper on Dr. William W. Mayo by Toomey: "Dr.
             Mayo was always ready to do his best to help those who were ill or
             in trouble and made it a rule never to ask who could pay. He went
             when called and ministered first. No matter if a call came from a
             remote part of Olmsted County he and his faithful buggy horse,
             "Messenger," were soon on the way to relieve the suffering. . . . Socially
             and professionally he treated all honest men alike and measured men
             by their worth and not by their wealth. He was a democrat in princi-
             ple and in politics and believed that every man, woman, and child
             was entitled to a fair showing."

Pages 13-14 **O'Connell MR:** *John Ireland and the American Catholic Church.*
             This text describes the lifetime relationship of Thomas O'Gorman with
             John Ireland. **Pages 202** and **203** depict young Father O'Gorman in
             Rochester.

Pages 13-14   *The Daily Post and Record.* **Rochester, MN, June 2, 1915.**
This article notes that Thomas O'Gorman, then bishop of Sioux Falls, spoke at the public ceremonies dedicating a bronze statue of Dr. William W. Mayo and recalled their friendship over many years. A record of this article is available at the Olmsted County History Center, Rochester, Minnesota.

Saint Marys Hospital Annals, pp 5-6.
Biographical note on O'Gorman: ". . . In January 1866, he was appointed pastor of Saint John's Church, Rochester, Minnesota, and held that pastorate until October 1877. From 1890 to 1896 he was a member of the faculty of the Catholic University, Washington, D.C.; in 1896 he was appointed bishop of Sioux Falls; he died in Sioux Falls September 18, 1921. His pastorate in Rochester was fruitful in vocations to the priesthood and to the religious life. Among his parishioners were the Most Reverend James John Keane, Rt. Reverend Patrick R. Heffron, Rt. Reverend J. J. Lawler, Reverend John Walsh, Reverend Stephen Condron, Brother Cyril of the Brothers of the Christian Schools (John O'Rourke), and five of the first seven postulants admitted to the Congregation of Our Lady of Lourdes, Rochester."

CHAPTER 2

Mother Alfred Moes

*T*he long-awaited day for Maria and Catherine Moes had arrived. On September 27, 1851, they left homeland and family in Remich, Luxembourg, to sail for the United States. Maria Moes, who later became Mother Alfred, founded two congregations of Franciscan Sisters, the first in Joliet, Illinois, the second in Rochester, Minnesota. A pioneer in health care, Mother Alfred founded Saint Marys Hospital and made an incalculable contribution to the Sisters' Story. The following chapter on the life of this astonishing woman focuses on her experiences that contributed to the founding of the hospital.

Born in 1828, Maria was 22 when she came to the United States; her sister Catherine, who accompanied her, was 30. Their father, Peter Gerard Moes, was a successful ironsmith in Remich. He inherited the trade from his father. At 27, he married Anna Botzem, 19, daughter of an old Remich family. Peter and Anna had eight surviving children, five girls and three boys. Maria was the youngest of the Moes family. Relatively well educated for women of their time, Maria and Catherine were the only children of their family to go away for their education. After private tutoring at home, they went to boarding school in Metz, a French city about 30 miles south of their home in Luxembourg. In Metz, they learned French and German and increased their skills in needlework, painting, singing, and other arts regarded as major accomplishments for young ladies. The younger Maria was energetic, confident, and quick, whereas Catherine, less healthy and robust, was more reticent than her sister. Their boarding school experience undoubtedly strengthened the bond that already existed between the two sisters.

Remich, Luxembourg, birthplace of Reverend Mother Mary Alfred Moes. The Moes residence was the fifth house to the left of the bridge. (From the Assisi Heights Archives, Rochester, MN.)

While in Metz, Maria and Catherine heard John Martin Henni, the first bishop of the Wisconsin Territory, speak about the frontier church in the United States. His compelling speech and the opportunity to meet with him made a remarkable impression on Maria and Catherine. They resolved to commit their lives to the frontier church and began preparations to leave. Undoubtedly, it was Maria who took the initiative on this decision, and throughout their lives her older sister followed her lead. Significantly, they did not choose to join a missionary religious order in Europe. Had they done so, they might well have gone to the United States and served the church. Instead, they chose to strike out for themselves, presumably for several reasons. Religious Sisters had no guarantee where superiors might send them, and blood sisters typically were not assigned together. Most likely, European life and convents did not appeal to Maria. She looked for new frontiers and opportunities; moreover, she left little to chance if she could help it. Strong-willed, confident, and sometimes head-strong, Maria sought control of major situations throughout her life.

Maria and Catherine's departure contrasted considerably with that of Irish families described earlier who emigrated about the same time. Dempseys, Irelands, and O'Gormans fled their homeland to escape famine and persecution. Financially impoverished with meager educations, they were part of the Catholic underclass in a country that, for them, held little opportunity and great despair. In contrast, Maria and Catherine carried with them ample funds from a well-established family and arranged for more funds to follow upon their instruction. Their Catholic faith was, if anything, an advantage in Luxembourg, a predominantly Catholic country for 1,200 years.

Because Bishop Henni was their only contact in the United States, the Moes sisters went to his diocese in the new territory of Wisconsin and arrived in Milwaukee late in 1851. Bishop Henni's missionary zeal, which so impressed them in Metz, was even more evident in his assignment in Milwaukee. Alone in a new country, they were fortunate to count on Henni's assistance. The opportunity to observe his prowess as a frontier church leader was particularly auspicious for Maria as a future religious founder.

Born in Switzerland, John Martin Henni began his study for the priesthood in European universities. His choice to become a missionary brought him to the United States, where he completed his studies and was ordained in 1829. Young Father Henni's first assignment was "riding the circuit," serving the settlements on horseback, within a wide radius of Canton, Ohio. Most of his parishioners were German immigrants who hailed him "Apostle to the Germans" for his zeal on their behalf. Church leaders quickly recognized Henni's abilities and appointed him vicar general of the Cincinnati diocese in 1834. Among his accomplishments in Cincinnati, Father Henni organized the teaching of English for adults, wrote a catechism in German for children, started a library, introduced better church music, and planned a bilingual seminary to train native clergy. One of Henni's highest achievements was founding *Der Wahrheitsfreund*, the city's first German newspaper, which opposed slavery, prohibition, and autocracy.

It was his successful work in Ohio that led to his appointment as bishop of the Wisconsin Territory. On May 4, 1844, Henni stepped onto the dock in Milwaukee at three in the morning with Father Michael Heiss, a priest colleague from Cincinnati who accompanied him. No one was on the dock to welcome them that night, and they waited to search for St. Peter's Church and their friend, Father Martin Kundig, one of five priests in the Wisconsin Territory: "As soon as dawn streaked the sky, Henni and Heiss, bag in hand, set out for St. Peter's Church. Early risers who chanced to take note wondered perhaps who the two men were who so buoyantly strode up the unpaved streets. . . ."

Milwaukee was a rapidly growing city with rich farmland to the west and a natural harbor that made it a center of commerce for Wisconsin. Opportunities for employment attracted large numbers of immigrants, and the population soared from about 1,700 in 1840 to more than 20,000 in 1850. The city's rapid growth buoyed the optimism of some civic leaders, as noted by one Milwaukee editor: "The tide of emigration to the West seems to increase daily. . .what an enterprising spirit characterizes the American people. . . . In no other country have towns and villages sprung up so suddenly as this. Everything seems to go ahead with railroad velocity."

Foreign-born Catholics were the largest group of newcomers; by 1850 they made up 64% of the population. Milwaukee's original citizens greeted the wave of new immigrants with mixed feelings. Although new settlers meant further growth and prosperity, the large numbers of immigrants made their city seem foreign. Resentment of the increasing numbers of foreign-born residents prompted a rise of nativism, a movement that discriminated against immigrants, especially those who were Catholics. In Eastern cities, anti-Catholicism sometimes expressed itself violently. Milwaukee citizens, although more restrained, worried about the large numbers of poor, illiterate immigrants who exacerbated the city's serious problem of providing human services.

As early as the fall of 1846, newspapers described Milwaukee as a "plague-ridden city," where streets were unpaved and animals roamed freely, leaving excrement and disease. The city was unable to control the distribution of milk from tubercular cows or to contain the spread of small-pox, typhus, diphtheria, and tuberculosis. Faced with an increasing death rate, the city's immediate needs were caring for the sick and providing for orphans. Establishing schools was another priority; only a third of the children attended any school at all. Of the 13 schools in the city at that time, 9 were private and required tuition.

Bishop Henni quickly assessed the needs of Milwaukee settlers and brought his considerable knowledge and experience to bear on the problems. His years of study for the church in Europe and the United States gave him a good grasp of persons with expertise and funds whom he might enlist to help him. During his assignment in Cincinnati, the Sisters of Charity impressed him. Indeed, the order, founded by Vincent de Paul, was universally respected for work in hospitals, schools, and orphanages. Elizabeth Bayley Seton had established an American branch, and Bishop Henni sought the Sisters' assistance for Milwaukee.

New Year's Day, 1845, Henni wrote Mother Xavier Clark in Emmitsburg, Maryland, and asked her to send "two or three of the Sisters of your Community." He went on to explain that he wanted to establish a small school and hoped other works would follow: "The time is not far off when we [will] want a Hospital . . . and before all, Asylums for poor orphans." Henni received no response from Mother Clark, who presumably was deluged with such requests. He wrote again the following June, perhaps more persuasively. His letter prompted a young candidate, Agnes Frances Flanley, to respond, "Oh, I would like to go to such a place as that." The next year, 3 days after she made vows, Sister Mary Agnes went to Milwaukee along with Sisters Simeon Burns and Mary Ann Paul. Father Martin Kundig went to Emmitsburg to accompany the Sisters on their journey to Milwaukee.

Within 2 weeks the Sisters started a school in the basement of St. Peter's Church. They soon found themselves spending more time going door to door caring for the sick than teaching pupils in the classroom. Such scattered treatment was inadequate in the face of increasing disease and the threat of cholera. The Sisters believed Milwaukee needed a hospital and Bishop Henni concurred, although such an idea was a radical one for any city at that time. Most people viewed hospitals as pestholes, set up to protect the public from disease by isolating the sick, rather than caring for them. The Sisters of Charity, however, operated hospitals whose quality stood in striking contrast. Their institutions maintained high standards, and Sister-nurses served patients with competence and respect.

Early in 1848, Bishop Henni went to Emmitsburg to speak with the Sisters of Charity about opening a hospital. Only weeks after his request, four more Sisters of Charity arrived in Milwaukee. They made immediate plans for the hospital and appealed in local newspapers "for aid to procure the necessary outfit of furniture." They also published their principles for operating the hospital, which included a policy against unwanted religious counseling: "Any patient may call for any clergyman he may prefer. But no minister, whether Protestant or Catholic, will be permitted to preach to, to pray aloud before, or interfere religiously with, such patients as do not ask for the exercise of his office. The rights of conscience must be held paramount to all others."

The well-established reputation of the Sisters of Charity and their clear stand against discrimination had important consequences for Milwaukee. The Milwaukee City Medical Association approved the hospital, and physicians from all sections of the city joined the staff. The Sisters opened

St. John's Infirmary, later known as St. Mary's Hospital, on Monday, May 15, 1848, with this official announcement: "The house is large, commodious, and built in the healthiest part of the city. . . . As the Sisters of Charity are to be the only nurses and attendants in the house, none need fear the absence of sympathy and eager vigilance. The very title and profession of a daughter of St. Vincent de Paul are sufficient guarantees to the public, that there will be no departure from the strictest order, the greatest cleanliness, and the most unremitting attention."

The Sisters found themselves caring for the sick, not only in the hospital but also out in the Milwaukee community.

In October 1850, a year before the Moes sisters arrived in Milwaukee, a ship with 300 passengers docked at the port of Milwaukee. Enroute from Norway and Sweden, most of the passengers were afflicted with typhus. Terrified Milwaukee citizens called it the "plague ship" and turned to their hospital for help. The mayor took over several government buildings at the harbor for housing the ill and called on the Sisters of Charity. Twenty-four hours a day for more than 3 weeks the Sisters cared for the typhus victims. One of them wrote later: "There were 260 patients, of whom sixty recovered, and all the others died."

The Sisters met this challenge and countless others, and their dedication helped overcome anti-Catholic sentiment in Milwaukee. The press was effusive in its praise: ". . . amidst scenes often most trying, did the Sisters of Charity continue their work when Death's daily victims were counted by tens and twenties. The community, grateful and thankful for the noble spirit that knows no color or creed, offered some compensation for services gracefully rendered. The compensation was respectfully declined."

Bishop Henni wrote Archbishop Reisach of Munich about the new hospital: "The charitable spirit of Catholics has won the admiration of Protestants for our religion and its endeavors. I found that well-to-do Protestants were the outstanding benefactors of this fine institution who, because of their own serious denominational differences, could not accomplish anything similar."

The accomplishments of the Sisters of Charity were not lost on Maria Moes after she arrived and began to assess opportunities on the new frontier.

Bishop Henni introduced Maria and Catherine Moes to the School Sisters of Notre Dame. These Sisters belonged to a thriving new teaching order from Germany, and he had persuaded them to teach in his diocese. Presumably, at Bishop Henni's suggestion, Maria and Catherine became candidates for membership in the School Sisters of Notre Dame. Only fragments of information exist about their 3 years in Milwaukee and their association with the School Sisters of Notre Dame. Of significance, they received excellent English instruction by two Georgetown University priests assigned by Bishop Henni as instructors for the congregation. As a future religious leader, Maria had the good fortune to have Mother Caroline Friess for superior and novice instructor.

Historians recognize Mother Caroline as "one of the most dynamic leaders of nineteenth century America." Josephine Friess, later Mother Caroline, was born in 1824 in a suburb of Paris to a French mother and a German father. Educated by private tutors and Benedictine nuns, she joined the School Sisters of Notre Dame at an early age. Her biographer notes that

Mother Caroline was a woman "of fine presence and strikingly beautiful as a young woman." When an artist was asked to paint her portrait, he replied, "Why, it would take me three months to paint those eyes! And then perhaps not do justice to them." At the age of 23, Mother Caroline came to the United States from Germany as companion to Mother Theresa Gerhardinger, founder of the School Sisters of Notre Dame. They traveled across the country by riverboat, lake steamer, wagon, stagecoach, and railroad to discover for themselves how their congregation could serve.

Before she returned to Germany, Mother Theresa appointed her 26-year-old companion as head of the congregation's schools in North America and directed her to build a motherhouse in Milwaukee. Mother Caroline arrived in Milwaukee on December 15, 1850, and in 3 weeks began the congregation's first school.

Mother Caroline Friess led the School Sisters of Notre Dame in North America for 42 years. (From Celebrating Woman of the 90's. M. Caroline Friess: 1824-1892 [Booklet]. Archives of the School Sisters of Notre Dame, Milwaukee, WI.)

She concentrated on staffing parish schools rather than building select academies for young women, as was often the custom for religious orders. In the face of Milwaukee's dire need for schools, the Sisters opened their classrooms to children of all races, faiths, and nationalities. This decision was characteristic of Mother Caroline, who saw needs and responded to them: "Were there orphans? The sisters would care for them. The place was poor? She would find funds and dedicated teachers. Too far away? She would travel there and see what could be done. . . . She received women of all cultures and nationalities into her congregation. She helped other religious congregations get started—even encouraging some of her own young candidates to join them. 'We are all serving the same God!'"

In 1855, Maria and Catherine Moes left the School Sisters of Notre Dame before making religious vows. Archives of the congregation contain a brief note, handwritten in German, about their departure. Maria was dismissed September 20 "for want of a calling" and "for lack of religious spirit." Two months later, Catherine "left with permission for want of a calling."

Maria and Catherine never revealed that they had joined the School Sisters of Notre Dame and that they later were asked to leave the congregation. They merely referred to their years in Milwaukee as "a period when we learned English." Such fragments of information about this critical time pose questions, among them: did they leave Europe intending to join an American religious order, or did the conditions they found on the frontier recommend this choice? Non–English-speaking single women without family in a frontier city most certainly had limited choices. Presumably, they preferred joining a religious congregation over returning to Luxembourg. Always the realist, Maria probably believed their choice offered some important opportunities. Among them, they would learn English, essential for them if they remained in the United States. As for a lifelong commitment to the congregation, they had sufficient time to make up their minds before making vows. On the whole, the experience worked to their advantage and helped prepare them for new lives on the frontier.

After 3 years in Milwaukee, no record exists about Maria and Catherine for more than a year after they left the School Sisters of Notre Dame. In December 1856, they asked to join the Sisters of the Holy Cross, but at no time gave their reasons for choosing this specific congregation. The Holy Cross order was a French order of religious sisters, brothers, and priests that sent missionaries around the world. In 1841 Father Edward Sorin, a Holy Cross priest, went to Indiana accompanied by six religious brothers and founded the University of Notre Dame. Two years later four Sisters joined him; in a short time, American women began requesting membership. As increasing numbers entered the congregation, the Sisters expanded their educational works.

Father Sorin looked for an American to lead the Sisters' congregation because he believed that superiors in France could not fully understand the American church. In March 1853, he met Eliza Maria Gillespie en route from the East to join the Sisters of Mercy in Chicago. She and her mother had stopped in South Bend to visit Eliza's younger brother, a Holy Cross seminarian. Well-educated with important family and political connections, 29-year-old Eliza Gillespie had experience in nursing and teaching. Father Sorin persuaded Eliza to stay in South Bend and join the Holy Cross congregation; she became Mother Mary of St. Angela. Within the year, Sorin sent Mother Angela to France for religious and academic training. Back from France, Mother Angela made major curriculum changes in the congregation's schools. These included advanced courses in science and higher mathematics, foreign languages taught by teachers in their native tongues, art and music offered by recognized artists, and a program of philosophy and theology.

About the same time that Mother Angela instituted her educational changes, Maria and Catherine entered the congregation. They received new names in religion; Maria became Sister Alfred and Catherine became Sister Barbara. They kept these names for the rest of their lives. Their novitiate lasted a year; the routine was rigorous, combining both spiritual exercises and secular studies. Novices rose at 4:30 a.m., began a set of spiritual exercises at 5:00 a.m., and had a period of study before breakfast. The balance of the morning included classes and study, then prayer and reflection before the noon meal. The afternoon was similar, with spiritual exercises, classes, and study. A period of recreation followed the evening meal. They retired at 9:00 p.m.

In 1858, Sisters Alfred and Barbara made final vows. A year earlier, Sister Alfred received her first teaching assignment in La Porte, Indiana, where she remained for a year and then went to another Indiana assignment. In 1861, she returned to La Porte, this time as directress of the school. During her second assignment in La Porte, a local priest, Father James Lawler, and his bishop, John Henry Luers of Fort Wayne, accused Sister Alfred of favoring German-speaking pupils. Further, Bishop Leurs wrote Father Sorin that Sister Alfred "acted very imprudently and little becoming a religious." She was out at night practicing in the choir of the German church and went to the fair and Strawberry Festival, "contrary to the express prohibition of the pastor!!" In a letter to Bishop Luers, Sister Alfred strongly objected to these charges. Superiors of her Holy Cross congregation, however, did not take her part. They chastised her "for serious disobedience to religious superiors" and at Christmastime 1861 sent her to St. John, Indiana. Three years later, the General Council of the Sisters of the Holy Cross voted to dismiss Sister Alfred Moes for "repeated disobedience to the Bishop and her legitimate Superiors." The superiors asked Sister Barbara to return to the motherhouse or consider herself no longer a member of the congregation. Characteristically, Sister Barbara followed Sister Alfred's lead and left the Holy Cross congregation.

In later years Mother Alfred made only general references to her life as a Holy Cross Sister; she attributed leaving the congregation as an arrangement made by the separation of the American order from France. Ambiguity, misunderstanding, and personal conflict characterized much of the period that Mother Alfred spent with the Sisters of the Holy Cross. On balance, however, she gained a great deal; among the opportunities the Sisters offered was a solid religious formation and an excellent education. In addition, her major superior was Mother Angela, a woman of outstanding ability who, like Mother Caroline in Milwaukee, made an inestimable contribution to the American church.

Mother Angela's response as a religious leader during the Civil War has significance for the Sisters' Story of Saint Marys Hospital. At the outbreak of the Civil War in April 1861, the Union had no army nurse corps, ambulance service, field hospital service, or organized medical corps. After the first battle, nurses became imperative. The Holy Cross Sisters were among 12 religious orders, 600 Sisters in all, that volunteered their services. Within months, Mother Angela established eight military hospitals and staffed two hospital ships. Her dynamism and determination helped turn 80 teachers into nurses in record time for service to the injured. Later, as a religious leader, Mother Alfred undoubtedly recalled this example when she responded to a public disaster and founded a hospital.

Sister Alfred was 35 years old with 13 years of frontier experience when she left the Sisters of the Holy Cross. Her commitment to the church and dedication to pioneers on the American frontier were perhaps even stronger than when she immigrated at age 22. The intervening years taught Sister Alfred a great deal—about frontier life, about the American Catholic church, about religious life and leadership, and, most of all, about herself. Sister Alfred made a major life decision at that time. She had served in two religious orders and followed the directives of others. She would establish a new congregation and shape its mission according to her own lights. That she chose to found an order to teach on the frontier fit well with her experience. What is not clear is her reason for becoming a Franciscan, and she never explained this choice.

Sister Barbara and two other former Holy Cross Sisters joined Sister Alfred, who initiated a request for affiliation with the Franciscan Friars at Allegheny, New York. Father Pamfilo, Custos Provincial of the Friars, granted their request and sent them the Franciscan Rule. He designated a Franciscan friar in Indiana to invest them into the order on June 1, 1863. A few months later, Father Carl Kuemin from Joliet, Illinois,

During the Civil War, Mother Angela Gillespie and her Holy Cross Sisters established eight military hospitals and staffed two hospital ships. (From the Annals of the Congregation of the Sisters of the Holy Cross: A Story of Fifty Years. Notre Dame, IN: The Ave Maria, p 132 [published prior to 1922].)

asked Sister Alfred to staff his parish school. Sister Alfred went with Sister Bernard, another Franciscan, to Joliet and within 2 months opened classes in the parish school for girls. Bishop James Duggan of Chicago, with authority for Joliet, approved the first Franciscan congregation of Sisters in Illinois.

At first the Sisters rented the second floor of a nearby house, but within a few months Sister Alfred purchased a house and two adjoining lots. With more room they took in boarders from among the girls attending school. To supplement their meager parish salaries, the Sisters created paper flowers, banners, and church articles. Working after school and late into the night, they enlisted help from their boarders. From the outset, the enterprising Sister Alfred never let lack of money stand in the way of building capital investments. One of the boarders, Mary Ann Rosenberger, asked to join the small community. In August 1865, Sister Alfred took her to Allegheny, where she received the Franciscan habit and a new name in religion, Sister Angela. At the end of the ceremonies, Father Pamfilo appointed Sister Alfred the first Mother General of the Franciscan Sisters, and the Joliet convent was designated as their motherhouse.

The pattern of the next years was one of growth and expansion. Confidently, Mother Alfred accepted new members and developed staff for schools. Between 1867 and 1872, 79 women entered the Joliet Franciscan congregation. Mother Alfred purchased property, built schools, and established convents. She opened six schools in Illinois and then expanded into Missouri, Ohio, Wisconsin, and Tennessee. Mother Alfred's source of support came largely from the Sisters who worked untiringly under her direction. Father Pamfilo continued to give her advice from Allegheny and served as an important Franciscan link with the larger church in Rome. Back in Chicago, Bishop Duggan was content to delegate direction of the congregation to the Franciscan Fathers.

The steady pattern of growth for the Joliet Franciscans, however, began to take a negative turn. The precipitating cause for the change was Bishop Duggan's removal from office for mental illness in 1869. The bishop's debilitating illness and "inconstancy of purpose and action" had serious consequences for the large diocese. Further, the Chicago fire of 1871 gutted the center of the city and the diocese lost seven churches, rectories, and schools at a cost of $1 million. For a year Chicago was without a bishop, which exacerbated the situation. Finally, in March 1870, Thomas Foley from the Archdiocese of Baltimore received the appointment. Bishop Foley inherited a dysfunctional diocese and faced the extensive capital expenses from ravages of the Chicago fire. Unlike his gracious, outgoing predecessor, Bishop Foley was solitary and uncommunicative; after his death, the Chicago diocesan paper had this description of Bishop Foley: "He never crossed the line into laymen's affairs. . . . His absolute seclusion within his own dominions may have deprived the people of Chicago who did not come in contact with him frequently of a just appreciation of the bishop's character. Nor was it enough to meet him once or twice; a certain austere dignity in his manner was liable to be misconstrued into hauteur . . . some have found his presence for the first time chilly and embarrassed. . . ."

Bishop Foley was accustomed to wielding authority from his years in America's premier diocese, where he served as chancellor, vicar general, and administrator to the archbishop. Moreover, at that time, the Vatican considered the United States "missionary territory" and gave bishops almost unlimited authority. He came to Chicago unacquainted with the frontier and with little pastoral experience. As the Joliet Franciscans would learn, the bishop used his considerable authority in a dogmatic, arbitrary manner.

Abruptly, without consultation or explanation, Bishop Foley terminated the Joliet Sisters' official relationship with the Franciscan Fathers, announced the election of a new general superior, and declared Mother Alfred ineligible for election. The Sisters had little recourse; he forced them to follow his directives or lose church approval for the congregation. They disagreed among each other over candidates for election, and serious division ensued within the order. Ultimately, they elected a new general superior, Sister Alberta Stockoff. Differences among the Sisters continued, however, and convinced Mother Alfred "that her very presence in the Motherhouse was a hindrance."

During this time a request came to Mother Alfred from Waseca, Minnesota. The pastor, with the blessing of Bishop Thomas Grace in St. Paul, asked her to "establish an institution for the education and training of young girls." A similar request came from St. Patrick's School in Eau Claire, Wisconsin. Mother Alfred believed these requests offered a propitious opportunity to remove herself from Joliet. Moreover, she knew the congregation had considerable money in the treasury that could be used for such an undertaking. These funds, raised to build a new academy, remained available because Bishop Foley had refused to approve the project.

The new general superior regretted the departure of her old friend, but she saw the wisdom of Mother Alfred's leaving. In a December 23, 1876, letter, she sanctioned the project, gave Mother Alfred authority to use congregational funds, and assigned Sisters to accompany her. When Bishop Foley learned of Mother Alfred's plan, he forcefully tried to prevent her from leaving. He did not succeed, however, and she left for Eau Claire early in the new year of 1877. On that long journey to the north by train and stagecoach, Mother Alfred must have reflected on the devastating recent events and on all of her life in the United States. She was 48 years old, 26 years in the United States, and 13 years founder and superior of the Joliet Franciscans. The future lay unknown before her in the north. Characteristically, she would pray for her enemies and commit her way to God. All things were possible.

ENDNOTES

Pages 19-21   **Kraman C:** *Odyssey in Faith: The Story of Mother Alfred Moes.*
Rochester, MN: Sisters of Saint Francis, Assisi Heights, 1990.
This text provides a valuable resource for documentation of Mother
Alfred's life.

Pages 20-21   Background information on Bishop John Henni and selected quotes
are from the following sources:
New Catholic Encyclopedia, **"Henni JM." Vol 6. Washington, DC:**
Catholic University of America, 1967, pp 1017-1018.

                Heiss M: Letter to the editor, May 5, 1844. *Der Wahrheitsfreund,* **May**
23, 1844. Quoted by Ludwig MM: *Right-Hand Glove Uplifted: A*
Biography of Archbishop Michael Heiss. **New York: Pageant Press,**
1968, p 140.

Page 22   *Milwaukee Sentinel,* **May 26, 1845. Cited by Walch T: Catholic**
Social Institutions and Urban Development: The View from
Nineteenth-Century Chicago and Milwaukee. *Catholic Historical*
Review **64 no. 1, January 1978, pp 25-26.**

Pages 22-24   **Quinn BW, Langill ED:** *Caring for Milwaukee: The Daughters of*
Charity at St. Mary's Hospital. **Milwaukee, WI: Milwaukee**
Publishing Group, 1998, pp 8-15, 17-19.
Commemorating 150 years of the hospital's service to Milwaukee, the
text contains extensive historical accounts and illustrations about St.
Mary's Hospital's remarkable history. The Sisters of Charity, who
founded St. Mary's Hospital, Milwaukee, in 1848 are now called the
"Daughters of Charity."

Page 24   The account of the plague ship is contained in an unpublished paper
entitled "St. Mary's Hospital, Milwaukee: 1848-1963," housed at the
Archives, Daughters of Charity of St. Vincent de Paul, Mater Dei
Proventialate, Evansville, Indiana.

Page 24   *Milwaukee Sentinel,* **April 27, 1855; October 22, 1856; August 8, 1864.**
Cited by Walch T: Catholic Social Institutions and Urban
Development: The View from Nineteenth-Century Chicago and
Milwaukee. *Catholic Historical Review* **64 no. 1, January 1978, p 29.**

Page 24   **Letter cited by Walch (p 30).**
Bishop Henni to Archbishop Reisach of Munich, March 26, 1859.

Pages 25-26   *Celebrating Woman of the 90's. M. Caroline Friess: 1824-1892* [Booklet]. **Archives of the School Sisters of Notre Dame, Milwaukee, WI.**

A copy of the document of dismissal, handwritten in German, from the Archives of the School Sisters of Notre Dame, Milwaukee, WI, is in the Congregational Archives, Sisters of Saint Francis.

Page 26   **Kraman C: *Odyssey in Faith: The Story of Mother Alfred Moes*, p 39.**

Page 26   Reference to Mother Alfred's dismissal from the Holy Cross congregation is contained in General Council minutes of December 12, 1864, available in Congregational Archives, Sisters of the Holy Cross, St. Mary's, Notre Dame, IN.

Pages 27-29   **Kraman C: Chapter 3. Indiana (1856-1863), pp 47-69.** Background on this period of Mother Alfred's life.

Costin GM: *Priceless Spirit*. Notre Dame, IN: University of Notre Dame Press, 1994. General background on the Holy Cross Sisters.

Page 28   **Steward GC Jr: *Marvels of Charity: History of American Sisters and Nuns*. Huntington, Indiana: Our Sunday Visitor Publishing Division, 1994, pp 139-140, 185, 188, 203.**

Farren S: *A Call to Care: The Women Who Built Catholic Healthcare in America*. St. Louis: Catholic Health Association of the United States, 1996, pp 9-11.

The remarkable story of Mother Angela Gillespie and the Holy Cross Sisters during the Civil War.

Pages 28-31   Detailed information about Mother Alfred's founding and dismissal from the Joliet Franciscans is available in the Congregational Archives of the Sisters of Saint Francis, Assisi Heights, Rochester, MN.

Kraman (pp 71-128).

Page 30   *The New Catholic Encyclopedia*, "Foley T." **Vol 3. Washington, DC: Catholic University of America, 1967, pp 560-561.**

The New World 8, no. 33, April 14, 1900, cited by Kraman, p 127.

CHAPTER 3

Vision and Achievement

$\mathcal{M}$ other Alfred Moes stayed in Eau Claire just long enough for the Sisters to get settled in St. Patrick's School. Her attention focused on building an academy in Minnesota, and she went to Waseca early in 1877. She and the Waseca pastor and parishioners failed to reach an agreement on the academy. Publicly, the issue was reported as a disagreement over the school's location. Internal sources, however, attribute the problem to a difference of nationalities. Waseca's predominantly Irish parishioners did not want to have Sisters with German backgrounds teaching their children. Hearing of the impasse, Father Francis Pribyl, from nearby Owatonna, quickly stepped forward to suggest his city as a future site for the school. Mother Alfred agreed to his proposal and promptly signed contracts to expedite construction. The *Owatonna Journal* commented on the undertaking when, in April, they announced the new academy; a month later the newspaper described the Sisters' school: "[Built] of brick and is to be fifty feet long, thirty-two feet deep and three stories high with a mansard roof. The cost will be eight thousand dollars."

The Owatonna school was well under way when Father Thomas O'Gorman invited Mother Alfred to build another academy in Rochester. Parishioners from St. John's and St. Bridget's parishes in Rochester resolved to raise $2,800 to buy land for the new academy. The *Rochester Post* of June 1, 1877, noted: "It is a fact worth mentioning that the Catholics at their meeting for the raising of funds required to buy the site for the institution resolved not to ask any outside aid but relied entirely on their own membership for the money."

Mother Alfred decided the congregation could afford to build both new schools. She purchased eight lots in Rochester, engaged an architect, and spent a busy spring and summer planning and supervising construction. In early summer, as the Owatonna building neared completion, she went to Joliet and brought back seven Sisters for the Minnesota missions. In September, three more Sisters came to Minnesota to staff the academies. Presumably, Mother Alfred had little difficulty in recruiting Sisters for the Minnesota schools. Her executive abilities and success in building schools were well established; in addition, most of the Sisters were personally fond of and loyal to their foundress.

Classes began in Owatonna's Sacred Heart Academy on October 1, 1877, and 2 months later, Mother Alfred opened the Academy of Our Lady of Lourdes in Rochester. Both schools welcomed pupils of all faiths and accepted boarders and day students. In building these secondary schools, Mother Alfred answered a definite need of the people she served. State funds provided for elementary education, the University of Minnesota, and normal schools. Publicly supported high schools, however, came into existence slowly. In the 1860s, there were only three public high schools in Minnesota; by the 1870s, there were 17 high schools, largely supported by tuition fees. Most of these schools were small and housed in upper stories of buildings or in private homes. Mother Alfred's "Select Schools," as she liked to call them, offered an education far superior to what was commonly available. Franciscan academies

A classroom at Sacred Heart Academy, Owatonna, Minnesota, later named St. Mary's Academy, the first school built by Mother Alfred Moes. (From Saint Marys Hospital Archives.)

were well staffed with at least six Sisters, and opening enrollments exceeded 60 students. In addition, they were adequately housed in buildings built and equipped for their purpose, and ran for far longer terms than other high schools.

The two academies were scarcely in operation when Mother Alfred and her Sisters found themselves cut off from the Joliet congregation by the decree of Bishop Thomas Foley of Chicago. Just a year before, as noted earlier, the bishop had denied Mother Alfred reelection as major superior. Indeed, the ensuing turmoil within the congregation over her position precipitated Mother Alfred's leaving for Minnesota early in 1877. Foley's

Drawing done in 1877 of the original Academy of Our Lady of Lourdes, Rochester, Minnesota. Dedicated on December 8, 1877, a few weeks later it became the motherhouse of the new congregation of the Sisters of Saint Francis. (From the Assisi Heights Archives, Rochester, MN.)

arbitrary actions stemmed from his wish to control religious orders within his Chicago diocese along with their works. Presumably, he did not take kindly to Mother Alfred's strong leadership, nor did he approve of taking congregational funds for works outside his diocese. Before Christmas, Bishop Foley wrote a directive to the new mother general: "Sister Alfred, formerly Mother [Superior], henceforth is not to be regarded as belonging to your house. All intercourse and correspondence with her is to be stopped. . . . Furthermore, if any Sister in your house or on the missions have a desire to unite with Mother Alfred, give them the liberty to do so, but they are never to return to your house. . . ."

Eleven Sisters were with Mother Alfred in Minnesota. Of the four who came with her from the Joliet congregation, only one returned. Sister Barbara Moes, Mother Alfred's sister, had recently arrived from Joliet. Mother Alfred suspected something was awry with Bishop Foley and wanted her sister with her in Minnesota. Six novices who had joined within the year were also among the group. With the bishop's pronouncement, 14 Joliet Franciscans from other states joined the Minnesota Sisters: 10 came from parish schools in Illinois and Ohio, and 4 came from the Joliet motherhouse. All four of the Sisters at the parish school in Portsmouth, Ohio, came with their directress, Sister Matilda Wagner. Among the four who came from the Joliet motherhouse, one was Sister Matilda's sister. The women who left the Joliet congregation followed Mother Alfred out of loyalty and belief in her mission. In addition, like Sister Matilda and her sister, some were affiliated with members of the Minnesota group. Mother Alfred's biographer, Sister Carlan Kraman, O.S.F., describes the impact of this exodus on the Joliet Franciscan community: ". . . a total of twenty-five sisters—nearly one fifth of the entire community, left 'their parent house' at Joliet at the close of the year 1877 to form a new community at Rochester. Ninety-two sisters remained in the Joliet congregation and the vacancies in the schools . . . bore heavily on the community."

Undaunted, Mother Alfred began taking ecclesiastical and legal steps to establish her second religious congregation. She went first to St. Paul to consult with Bishop Thomas Grace. With a growing Catholic population, the bishop must have warmly welcomed this experienced group of teaching Sisters to his diocese. Bishop Grace appointed Mother Alfred general superior and authorized the new congregation. Mother Alfred then established the Rochester academy and convent as the new motherhouse and novitiate.

Life for postulants in the pioneer congregation was rigorous, but they never lacked recruits. The Dempseys' daughters, Mary and Julia, were among the first to join. In August 1878, they received the Franciscan habit and new religious names along with five other young women. Mary received the name Sister Passion, and Julia became Sister Joseph. Later, Sister Joseph recalled their lives as young Franciscans. They had wood and water to carry, snow to shovel, soap to make, lamps to clean, and many more backbreaking tasks. Yet their spirits remained high. She wrote that "It was 'all for God'; . . . these young recruits were willing and generous; their only anxiety was to keep their parents from finding out that they 'had it hard' in the convent, for sometimes visitors or the boarders reported things that the postulants tried to conceal."

Several families had more than one daughter enter the Rochester Franciscans. Patrick and Mary Dempsey had three Franciscan daughters; Mary and Julia's younger sister Helen followed them into the congregation. Their youngest daughter, Anna, had entered only a few days when Patrick put his foot down. With all the girls in the convent, the housework, laundry, and cooking now fell entirely to their mother. As his granddaughter, Sister Carmela Dempsey, told the story, Patrick marched to the convent, took a seat in the parlor, and refused to leave until he saw the mother superior. When she appeared, he told her, "Anna must come home, her mother needs her." And home she went that day.

In 5 years, the Rochester Franciscans more than doubled their numbers and established new schools in Minnesota, Ohio, and Kentucky: "Mother Alfred was again the head of a thriving community which was able to accept new schools because young women continued to join the ranks. Though the separation from Joliet had been painful and frustrating, the future was full of promise. Mother Alfred and her fifty-four companions with faith and courage moved into that future."

The six founding Sisters of Saint Marys Hospital entered the Rochester congregation during these years. They came from frontier farms and towns across the Midwest, and their entrance records indicate various ages, backgrounds, and experience. Sister Joseph Dempsey was 22 and prepared as an elementary teacher when she entered from St. John's parish, Rochester. Sister Fidelis Cashion, also from St. John's, entered at 28. Sister Constantine Koupal was 32 when she came; born in Bohemia, she was 12 when she arrived in the United States. Sister Fabian Halloran entered at 20 from Glencoe, Minnesota, with teaching credentials, and Sister Sienna Otto came at 18 from Winsted, Minnesota. Sister Sylvester Burke was the youngest, only 15 when she arrived from Pine Grove, Ohio. With the exception of Sister Constantine, all of the women were first-generation Americans of German or Irish descent. Although these Sisters eventually would be assigned to Saint Marys Hospital, their first assignments were in teaching; at the time they entered, education was the congregation's only work. The dramatic events that changed the work of these Sisters from teaching to nursing were the beginning of "the miracle in a cornfield," and the miracle started with a tornado.

Tuesday, August 21, 1883, was a hot, humid day for Rochester residents, who watched black storm clouds roll in from the northwest late in the afternoon. Between 5:30 and 5:45 p.m., the barometer fell 2 inches, followed by a heavy downpour of rain. A large group from the Congregational Church, including 100 children, had just returned from a picnic and waited in the church annex for the rain to stop. A few miles to the east, a farmer near Chester saw a large black funnel surrounded by a yellowish mist, 100 feet high. Whirling rapidly, it moved in a zigzag pattern almost a mile wide, throwing off boards and pieces of timber. Hail, 3 to 4 inches in diameter, accompanied the wind. The tornado that started as a windstorm near

Rochester tornado, August 21, 1883. (Top, Elmer and Tenney photographers. By permission of the Minnesota Historical Society. Bottom, From Saint Marys Hospital Archives.)

Sioux City, Iowa, and passed Owatonna as a violent gale approached Rochester from the northwest. It moved eastward through the city and caused the greatest destruction in north Rochester, called Lower Town. At a home just west of Rochester, the tornado picked up a little desk clock and set it down unharmed some distance from the house. The clock had stopped at 24 minutes to 7.

About 6 o'clock that evening, young Dr. William J. (Will) Mayo and his brother Charles H. (Charlie) Mayo, a medical student, rode north to the slaughterhouse for a sheep's head to use for practicing cataract operations. The workers, who headed for home in the approaching storm, urged the young men to do the same. Later, Charlie recalled the experience: "Doctor Will and I started home without the sheep's head. A terrible wind began to blow and just as we got across the bridge on North Broadway, the bridge tumbled down. A little farther on we saw two elevators fall. We got to the old Cook corner in time to see the cornice of the building blown off; part of it struck our horse; he got loose from the buggy and ran up Broadway and into a stone blacksmith shop. Doctor Will and I reached there just as its tin roof was blown off. . . . we kept close to the stone wall and watched the storm. . . . A little later when we were going up College Street, we heard there had been people injured so we went back to see what we could do for them."

The Academy of Our Lady of Lourdes was at the north end of the city. With student boarders away in August, only the Sisters and a number of new recruits were in residence. Sister Gabriel Hochgesung remembered that Mother Alfred called to the young women in the yard, "Come in, we're going to have a terrible storm!" They ran to the cellar, lying flat on the floor while the tornado roared like a railroad train over their heads. The Sisters feared the convent had blown away but found only minor damage, a hole in one corner of the tin roof. Other parts of Rochester, however, had extensive damage. Lower Town was a shambles. Houses were blown off their foundations, trees were stripped bare of leaves, and blades of grass pierced tree trunks like needles. Dead livestock littered the countryside, and the slaughterhouse was in ruins. A Rochester historian describes how citizens managed to get out a call for help: "Telegraph lines had snapped during the tornado. Someone jury-rigged a line into the main line, and on this feeble connection a message was tapped to Governor Lucius F. Hubbard. The code was chillingly brief: 'Rochester is in ruins. Twenty-four people were killed. Over forty are seriously injured. One-third of the city laid waste. We need immediate help.'"

Rescue work began at once. Physicians were quickly on the job as men searched with lanterns for the injured and carried them into hotels or offices. They brought 40 persons to the Sisters' convent and laid them on parlor floors until cots could be found. Dr. William Worrall Mayo, assisted by druggist George Weber, was in charge at the Buck Hotel at the edge of Lower Town. Sons Dr. Will and Charlie worked with patients brought to the Mayo office. Dr. W. W. Mayo soon realized that the city's emergency medical efforts needed reorganization. The next day he had the injured transferred from homes, offices, and the convent to an improvised hospital in Rommel's Dance Hall on Broadway and Center Street. The city council appointed Dr. W. W. Mayo in charge of the hospital, and several women volunteered as nurses: "At once Dr. Mayo saw the need for a better organization of the nursing staff. The volunteers were willing enough, but . . . they had homes and families to look after. It was urgently necessary to find nurses who could give their entire time to the job. . . . Next morning Dr. Mayo appeared early at the convent and said to the mother superior in his offhand way, 'There ought to be a sister down there to look after those fellows. . . .' Agreeing at once, Mother Alfred appointed two sisters to the task, and from then on until the hospital was closed, sisters supervised the nursing."

That same day Mother Alfred sent two postulants to Lower Town to see whether anyone in the stricken homes had been overlooked. At one home, they found a little girl with an empty coffeepot in one hand and a raw potato in the other. She told them, "Momma is sick and can't get up and she told me to see if I could find something to eat." The Sisters helped the child and her mother and as many others as they could. Although Mother Alfred was economical about convent money, she willingly gave it to persons in need: "Not out of her abundance but out of her poverty she used to send food and clothing where they were welcome and sometimes gave money to poor people to help tide them over a period of illness in their families."

Across the region, many others responded generously. Minneapolis and St. Paul each subscribed $5,000, Chicago $10,000, and Winona and St. Cloud each $3,000. Communities in the Dakotas, whom Rochester residents had helped a few years earlier when grasshoppers stripped their fields of crops, now gave socials and entertainments to raise funds and returned the kindness. The relief committee collected more than $60,000, which furnished clothing for 253 families, rebuilt 119 houses, and gave each family about $78.00 toward new furniture.

Within the next months, Rochester seemed to return to normal. Unknown to most, however, the tornado had triggered an idea in the mind of one person, and the city would never be the same. Mother Alfred was the person whose idea changed the future of Rochester, and the genesis of her idea bears examination. In the throes of the tornado's devastation, her first response had been the care of injured victims. Characteristically, after the tornado, she assessed how she and others in the Rochester community might have better served the sick and injured. It was imperative, she concluded, that Rochester have a hospital, and for Mother Alfred, "to think was to do." Credit for the idea of a Rochester hospital, however, has not always gone to Mother Alfred. One view claims the idea was Bishop John Ireland's, that he had recommended a hospital to her before the tornado. Examination of his papers and other contemporary sources does not support this position. Other accounts credit the Mayos, but, from the beginning, Dr. W. W. Mayo and his sons publicly and privately praised Mother Alfred for conceiving the idea. Another story attributes the idea to a clairvoyant dream of Mother Alfred's and describes how she saw into the future and envisioned a world-famous medical center in Rochester.

Mother Alfred's personal characteristics and life experiences provide convincing evidence that building a hospital in Rochester was indeed her own idea. An intelligent, pragmatic woman of faith, Mother Alfred used life experiences to solve practical problems. She was well acquainted with Sisters' hospitals in both Europe and the United States. Luxembourg, the land of her birth, had a long tradition of hospitals operated by vowed religious women. For centuries, hospitals and schools were the bedrock of Catholic benevolent institutions throughout Western Europe. As noted, when Mother Alfred first came to Milwaukee, she knew the Sisters of Charity and their hospital, which they opened to "all citizens or strangers without distinction of class, religion, or nation. . . ." Further, she

Mother Alfred Moes, O.S.F., founder of Saint Marys Hospital. (From Saint Marys Hospital Archives.)

recognized that such service for all persons decreased the degree of anti-Catholicism pervasive at the time. In Indiana, as a Holy Cross Sister, she had another experience with hospitals, when, in response to the critical needs of Civil War wounded, Mother Angela Gillespie established eight military hospitals and staffed two hospital ships. At that time the Holy Cross Sisters were exclusively a teaching order, but Mother Angela turned 80 Sister-teachers into Sister-nurses in record time to serve the injured. In summary, Mother Alfred had ample experience and sound reasons for conceiving the idea of a Catholic hospital in Rochester.

Within a short time, Mother Alfred approached Dr. W. W. Mayo with her idea about a hospital. Dr. Mayo gave this account of their conversation when he spoke at the ceremony for the first addition to the hospital in 1894: ". . . the Mother Superior came down to my office and in the course of her visit she asked, 'Doctor, do you not think a hospital in this city would be an excellent thing?' I answered, 'Mother Superior, this city is too small to support a hospital.' I told her too that the erection of a hospital was a difficult undertaking and required a great deal of money, and moreover we had no assurance of its success even after a great deal of time and money had been put into it.

'Very well,' she persisted; 'but you just promise me to take charge of it and we will set that building before you at once. With our faith and hope and energy, it will succeed.' I asked her how much money the Sisters would be willing to put into it, and her reply was, 'How much do you want?' 'Would you be willing to risk forty thousand dollars?' I said. 'Yes,' she replied, 'and more if you want it. Draw up your plans. It will be built at once.'"

Dr. W. W. Mayo's lack of enthusiasm for a hospital stemmed at least partly from personal experience. His first job in the United States was at Bellevue Hospital in New York "at its nadir of neglect and political exploitation." Later, as a physician, he was equally unimpressed with other U.S. hospitals. Most Americans of the time shared his negative view. Hospitals were grim, gloomy places where care was intermittent and sometimes entirely lacking. Even more importantly, this was a period in medical history before antisepsis; one did not go to a hospital to get well, but simply to die. Unknown to physicians and patients alike, the major risk came from the physician's hands, instruments, and clothes and from the dressings used. Physicians gave little thought to cleanliness. Operations usually took place in tiny, badly lit rooms, and the surgeon commonly kept in a closet an old, unwashed frock coat that he used repeatedly during surgical procedures.

Hospitals were charity asylums for the sick poor who had nowhere else to go, in the same class with poorhouses, jails, and insane asylums. Biographer Helen Clapesattle describes Minnesota hospitals of the time: "What hospitals there were in Minnesota in 1883 were concentrated in the Twin Cities and were not of a sort to attract paying patients. There were three in St. Paul, 'one an achievement, one a hope, and one a promise.' The achievement was St. Joseph's Hospital, the oldest and without doubt the largest and best equipped in the state; the hope was the City and County Hospital . . . and the promise was the Episcopalian St. Luke's, . . . housed in an old-fashioned residence, . . . one woman constituted the entire staff—superintendent, nurses, and dietitian all in one."

Despite the risks, Mother Alfred was determined to build a hospital, and for the next 4 years she directed a rigorous campaign to raise money for a building fund. By hard work and frugal living, the Sisters earned and saved every cent they could. They took in extra work and spent their scant leisure time giving music lessons and crocheting and embroidering linens for sale. Every durable gift with any monetary value went to the motherhouse for the building fund.

Carefully, Mother Alfred counted the nickels and dimes. She deposited all surplus earnings in the bank to be withdrawn only for new construction or permanent improvements. The Sisters' clothing was poor and coarse. Two-dollar shoes, which they got for $1.90, were the custom. Mother Alfred herself wore 50¢ cloth slippers when at home; while traveling she wore low, leather shoes that cost about $1.50. The Sisters sat down to plain, sometimes meager, meals. At the Rochester motherhouse and academy, for example, 5 pounds of round steak and a 15¢ soupbone were a day's supply of meat for a household of some 30 Academy boarders and from 12 to 20 Sisters and postulants. Their working hours were long. They chopped wood, made their own soap, and slept on pillowcases made of flour sacks. By constant labor and sacrifice, the Sisters raised money for the building fund.

When Mother Alfred determined that enough money had been saved for the hospital, Dr. W. W. Mayo chose the site—9 acres, just west of the city limits on Zumbro Street. Mother Alfred approved his choice. She liked the location, far enough from town to escape the noise and dust of city streets, yet close enough to be reasonably convenient. A visiting priest happened to meet Mother Alfred and Dr. Mayo as they returned from inspecting the new property. He recalled that Mother Alfred described the site as very choice with beautiful trees and shrubbery and wooded hills on three sides.

At an executive meeting of the congregation in July 1887, Mother Alfred asked the Sisters to approve building the hospital: 27 voted "yes," 4 voted "no." The fact that four Sisters voted against the hospital appears significant in view of later tensions within the congregation over the allocation of resources and personnel. The congregation, now 10 years old, had begun to establish its reputation in education. Requests came more frequently to staff parish schools and to expand the select academies. Presumably, those who voted against a hospital were teachers who feared it would undermine the congregation's work in education by diverting funds and personnel. Teaching Sisters had sacrificed and worked hard to serve pioneer pupils and build a reputation for congregational schools. A hospital, as everyone knew, was a highly uncertain venture; moreover, Rochester Franciscans had no hospital experience or training as nurses. Nevertheless, Mother Alfred's desire for a hospital prevailed, and she wrote Bishop Ireland for permission to begin the project. The bishop approved the project, and his secretary wrote that "the bishop was pleased with the plans." Two months later, the Sisters paid $2,200 cash to John Ostrum, a local farmer, for the hospital property. Construction, however, took another year to begin "because the Academy of Our Lady of Lourdes needed to add a wing immediately."

Dr. W. W. Mayo worked assiduously on plans for the building: "the hospital must be the best and most modern that means allowed." After he and his sons pooled their knowledge of hospitals, they needed more information on construction and management. Dr. W. W. Mayo took Dr. Will on a special tour of eastern hospitals to study floor plans, lighting arrangements, and administrative organization. They visited, among others, the new Methodist Episcopal Hospital in Brooklyn, and Dr. Henry P. de Forest showed them through the building. Long afterward Dr. de Forest recalled this visit by "a gentleman from the West dressed in a . . . Prince Albert coat of black broadcloth accompanied by his youthful son."

Returning from their tour of hospitals, the Doctors Mayo gave instructions to the architect they had selected and sent the plans back "once and twice and thrice" until they got exactly what they wanted. Mother Alfred awarded Winona contractor J. D. Billingsley the building contracts: $16,500 for the hospital and $2,200 for the heating plant. George Weber, a druggist, and Granville Woodworth, another building contractor, agreed to serve as bondsmen. All parties signed the contract on August 1, 1888. The Saint Marys annals tells the troubling, but fortuitous, story of the hospital's construction: "Work began immediately and was not suspended during the winter in spite of the cold which hindered progress. In the spring the situation looked dubious and there was a rumor that the contractor was going bankrupt. Mr. Charles McCloskey, a devoted friend of the Sisters, informed Mother Alfred of the rumor and advised her to take precautions against a lien on the convent property. That same day Mother Alfred had legal notices prepared warning all concerned that any accounts . . . not settled for by the contractor, should be referred to his bondsmen. These notices were tacked on trees near the convent property and on the hospital grounds."

A few days later Billingsley slipped out of town in the middle of the night. The next morning the building crew called on the bondsmen, George Weber and Granville Woodworth, and asked them what to do. They told the crew to finish the work. When Weber and Woodworth consulted with Mother Alfred, they learned that $13,550 had already been paid on the building and it was only half finished. They had only $3,000 left to pay the workers. As bondsmen, if the hospital was not completed by fall, they were liable for a daily $10 fine until the building was finished. George Weber could not afford to lose that much money. He had a family to support and a business to look after and feared that he might lose everything because of the hospital. "Many a night's sleep I lost over it," he recalled, "every dollar I had in the world was at stake." Woodworth took over direction of the construction and both men kept close watch on the work and costs. The hospital was completed within 2 months of the scheduled date, without any loss to the Sisters of Saint Francis and at no cost to the bondsmen.

Public interest in the hospital heightened as the building took shape. Mother Alfred and the Mayos endlessly discussed plans, considered policies, and speculated on the prospects of success. When Dr. Charlie expressed the opinion that the hospital would draw patients from "all these little towns around here," Mother Alfred proudly reported his words to the Sisters, who were in need of reassurance. In the evenings, townspeople walked or drove out in their buggies "to see how the hospital was coming along." As construction progressed, Rochester papers lengthened their periodic reports of the building. Their descriptions offer an interesting contemporary commentary: ". . . [The] 'imposing edifice,' [was] three stories high, built of brick with window ledges of roughhewn stone and four balconies on the west and north sides. A flight of stone stairs leads up to the large double doors, over which is a cut plate glass window with the inscription, 'St. Mary's

Saint Marys Hospital opened September 30, 1889, with 27 beds. (From Saint Marys Hospital Archives.)

Hospital, conducted by the Sisters of St. Francis.' The doors are placed in a large brick arch, the lower part of which consists of carved stone ornaments."

The papers described that the basement contained "dispensary rooms for outpatients, laundry and vegetable rooms, an immense cistern to hold five hundred gallons of water, and especially the 'foul air room' of the remarkable ventilating system that makes it 'an utter impossibility for foul air to remain in any part of the building.' . . . On the first floor, offices, reception parlors, dining room, pantry, and the kitchen, equipped with a large cooking range having an eighty-gallon boiler attachment from which hot water will be piped throughout the building.

On the second floor, [were] wards and private bedrooms and the operating room [described as] 'a credit to its deviser. Part of the room is built out in the same manner as a bay window, and as it is on the north side the light will fall upon the operating table from the north and the skylights above. Surgeons unite in the opinion that a north light is the proper light for operating purposes, hence this room must be perfect. The floor of the room is inclined a trifle and is so constructed that it can be flooded with water, which instead of running into the adjacent hall, will run into a waste pipe.'

And on the third floor, more wards and private rooms . . . [and] a chapel and sacristy for the sisters' devotions, and a large recreation room 'where patients will be able to walk around for exercise, or will be provided with suitable reading matter.'

The papers listed too the various bathrooms, closets, clothes chutes, the gaslight fixtures throughout, and the water faucets in the halls for use in case of fire. They were enthusiastic about the artistic staining of all the wainscoting and the beautiful floors of curly maple planed and rubbed to the smoothness of glass. . . . On the whole, they said, the building is neat, clean, and generally attractive, 'as handsome as any residence can be,' with every feature designed to make it pleasant and homelike for the sick. . . ." Sister Joseph noted in the Saint Marys' annals that one paper's description "should be taken with salt"; the editor, wanting to give a favorable account, described some features "that were only hoped for." In any case, the building was as complete as the experience of the Mayos and the funds of the Sisters could make it.

During the final days of construction, Sister Sienna, Sister Constantine, and Sister Hyacinth walked to the hospital every morning carrying their noon lunches. They cleared out rubbish, swept, dusted, and prepared rooms for patients. The hospital opened without formal ceremony, because the official blessing was scheduled for some weeks later. The Sisters had planned to open the hospital on October 1, 1889, but the Mayos had an operation to perform the day before and the operating room was ready: ". . . with a fine disregard for pomp and palaver they simply began. The operation was for the removal of a cancer of the eye; Dr. Charles Mayo performed it, Dr. W. J. Mayo assisted, and Dr. W. W. Mayo gave the anesthetic."

Within a week eight patients were admitted, Sisters Sienna, Constantine, Fidelia, and Hyacinth were assigned to duty in the hospital, and Edith Graham, a Rochester girl graduated from the school of nursing at the Women's Hospital in Chicago and the first trained nurse in town, was put in temporary charge of the nursing staff."

The Sisters opened the hospital "to all sick persons regardless of their color, sex, financial status, or professed religion." When the question arose whether Saint Marys Hospital was intended for Catholics only, Mother Alfred made the Sisters' position clear: "the cause of suffering humanity knows no religion and no sex; the charity of the Sisters of St. Francis is as broad as their religion."

Saint Marys Hospital was neither a charity asylum for the poor nor a nursing home for the wealthy. At a time when it was almost unknown for a hospital to serve both paying patients and charity cases, Saint Marys Hospital received all persons. The policy of admitting all persons and giving them equal care was important to the Doctors Mayo and the Sisters of Saint Francis. For the Sisters, care for each person, particularly for the poor, was at the heart of the gospel they espoused. The Mayos, probably motivated more by humanitarian sympathies, demonstrated unqualified respect and care for each patient.

Of significance for the Sisters' Story, the founder of the hospital was no longer in charge of the congregation when the hospital opened. Mother Alfred, whose vision and leadership made the hospital a reality, was, for the second time, required to give up her position as mother superior. Back in Joliet, it was the local bishop, Thomas Foley, who took issue with Mother Alfred. Foley arbitrarily denied her reelection as mother superior and subsequently ordered her to leave his diocese. In Rochester, the bishop also denied her reelection as mother superior. His action, however, was prompted by some of Mother Alfred's own Sisters who secretly complained to him about her. The bishop was John Ireland, recently appointed archbishop with ecclesiastical authority for Minnesota and the Dakotas. Later, Ireland confided his regret "for the inconsiderateness with which Mother Alfred had been treated and said of those who talked to him against her that he would never have believed that people could be so uncharitable as they were."

Nonetheless, a few months before the hospital opened, on July 14, 1889, Ireland went to the motherhouse for a visitation. Rochester pastor Father William Riordan, a good friend to the Franciscans, accompanied him. An unusually large number of Sisters assembled in chapel to hear the bishop. He announced that there would be an election for mother superior the following morning and that Mother Alfred was not a candidate for reelection. This unusual election, which occurred "about nine o'clock on the morning of the fifteenth," is described in the Saint Marys' annals: "When the Sisters had deposited their ballots in the urn, Bishop Ireland and Father Riordan began to scrutinize them, the Bishop reading the names aloud. Every vote apparently was for Mother Alfred. . . . The Bishop stopped reading and said . . . 'But I told you not to vote for Mother Alfred.' Then he spoke at some length to the Sisters but said nothing unfavorable to Mother Alfred.

At the end of his address he called on Sister Matilda to come forward and appointed her Superior General for a term of three years. . . . The Bishop said nothing against Mother Alfred and directed Mother Matilda to be 'nice and kind' to her."

After Mother Matilda's appointment, Bishop Ireland and Father Riordan departed, leaving the Sisters free to elect their first and second assistants. They elected Mother Alfred first assistant and Sister Stanislaus Kostka second assistant.

In contrast to those who complained to Bishop Ireland, most of the Sisters loyally supported Mother Alfred and her decisions. The Saint Marys' annals summarize this prevailing relationship: "Mother Alfred directed, controlled, inspired all the activities of the congregation. Corporation meetings that had been held were mostly a matter of form and the Constitutions did not prescribe a Council for the General Superior. The Sisters were all young and really incapable of giving her much assistance as advisers; Mother Alfred was from twenty to thirty years older than any of the others, except her sister; she had extensive experience, her executive abilities were unquestionable."

As noted earlier, four Sisters had voted against Mother Alfred's proposal for a hospital. Presumably, they favored retaining education as the congregation's sole ministry and the recipient of all resources. Likely the same rationale and concerns prompted these Sisters to speak against Mother Alfred to Bishop Ireland. Such early instances of division presage future conflict over resources among congregational members in high places as the Sisters' Story unfolds.

Mother Matilda and Mother Alfred worked closely together during the fall of 1889. The new 38-year-old mother superior learned quickly from her mentor, who had just turned 61. Mother Matilda asked Mother Alfred to assign the first Sisters to the hospital and within a short time also asked her to take charge as superintendent: "[Mother Alfred] threw herself into her new position . . . sometimes working continuous shifts of one day and night and another day. She carried water from the basement to the upper floors, delivered trays of food to patients, shoveled coal, and pinked oilcloth to make covers for the washstands in the patients' rooms."

Mother Alfred remained in charge of Saint Marys Hospital until the next August, when she went to Ironton, Ohio, to visit her sister, Sister Barbara. She stayed with her for several months, then moved to St. Paul, where many of her Sister friends were working. Mother Alfred spent much of her time in church praying. When told she might become ill from such long vigils in the cold building, she replied, "I must pray for my enemies. I don't know who they are, but I pray for all of them." It was the only evidence of bitterness she showed. When Dr. W. W. Mayo visited her and begged her to return to Saint Marys Hospital, she told him, "No, I can't come back, this is where God wants me to be."

Mother Alfred died in St. Paul, December 18, 1899, surrounded by Sisters, who brought her body back to Rochester. All of the Sisters who were charter members came for the funeral, some from very distant points. The motherhouse chapel was draped in mourning, and Bishop Joseph Cotter of Winona was the celebrant.

Father William Riordan, Mother Alfred's friend and Rochester pastor, gave the eulogy. He described Mother Alfred as a woman of strong mental powers and deep religious feeling. Father Riordan recalled the tornado when "she and her sisters who showed so much generosity towards the suffering, acquired their first experience in hospital work." He referred to her "noble achievements, especially to her crowning work," as he called it, "the establishment of Saint Marys Hospital in Rochester." Mother Alfred was buried in Rochester next to her beloved Sister Barbara, who preceded her in death 4 years earlier.

ENDNOTES

Pages 35-36   **Kraman C:** *Odyssey in Faith: The Story of Mother Alfred Moes.* **Rochester, MN: Sisters of Saint Francis, Assisi Heights, 1990, pp 119, 121.**

Owatonna Journal, **April 5, 1877; May 10, 1877.**
Articles on the new Sacred Heart Academy in their city.

Rochester Post, **June 1, 1877.**
Article about St. John's and St. Bridget's parishes.

Saint Marys Hospital Annals.
"The Catholics of the two parishes under Father O'Gorman, Saint John's, Rochester, and Saint Bridget's near the present village of Simpson, raised $2,800 to pay for a site for the new convent and academy. Father O'Gorman headed the subscription list with a donation of $25.00."

Pages 36-37   Academician Sister Emmanuel Collins, O.S.F., described the status of primary and secondary schools at this time in an unpublished paper, *"A Commentary on the Testament."* Congregational Archives, Sisters of Saint Francis, Rochester, MN.

Page 37   Bishop Thomas Foley to Mother Francis Shanahan, December 23, 1877. Congregational Archives, Sisters of Saint Francis, Rochester, MN.

Pages 37-38   **Hayes MFA:** *Years of Beginning, A History of the Sisters of the Third Order Regular of Saint Francis, of the Congregation of Our Lady of Lourdes, Rochester, Minnesota, 1877-1902.* **Unpublished Master's Thesis, Catholic University of America, Washington, DC, 1956.**
Excellent background information on the early years of the Rochester Franciscans.

Pages 37-38   **Kraman (pp 134-135).**

Page 38   **Saint Marys Hospital Annals, pp 7-8.**
Sister Joseph Dempsey's comments. The annals, available in Saint Marys Hospital Archives, provide an ongoing history of the hospital from 1889 to the present.

Pages 38-39   Sister Carmela Dempsey, O.S.F., Sister Joseph's niece, related this story about her aunts and her grandfather in an interview on October 4, 1998.

Page 39   **Kraman C:** *Odyssey in Faith: The Story of Mother Alfred Moes,* **p 157.**
                 The status of the Rochester Franciscans in 1882.

Pages 39-42   **Clapesattle H:** *The Doctors Mayo.* **Minneapolis: The University of**
                 Minnesota Press, 1941, pp 242-245.

                 Hodgson HW: *Rochester: City of the Prairie.* **Windsor Publications,**
                 1989, pp 25-26.

                 The story of Rochester's 1883 tornado.

                 Saint Marys Hospital Annals.
                 Firsthand memories of the event, dictated by Sister M. Gabriel
                 Hochgesung, O.S.F., are available in the Congregational Archives, Sisters
                 of Saint Francis, Rochester, MN.

Page 41   **Hodgson** describes Rochester citizens' call for help (**pp 25-26**).

Page 42   **Clapesattle** recounts Dr. W. W. Mayo's request to the Sisters (**p 244**).

Page 43   **Saint Marys Hospital Annals.**
                 Reference to Mother Alfred Moes.

Page 44   **Saint Marys Hospital Annals.**
                 Dr. W. W. Mayo's speech.

Page 45   **Clapesattle** describes Minnesota hospitals (**pp 247-248**).

Pages 45-46   **Hayes MFA:** *Years of Beginning, A History of the Sisters of the Third*
                 Order Regular of Saint Francis, of the Congregation of Our Lady of
                 Lourdes, Rochester, Minnesota, 1877-1902, **p 40.**

                 Saint Marys Hospital Annals.
                 Mother Alfred's careful savings practices.

Page 46   Details of the executive meeting of the congregation described in **Hayes**
                 (**p 41**).

Page 46   James G. Byrne (secretary to Archbishop Ireland) to Mother Alfred
                 Moes, August 29, 1887. Congregational Archives, Sisters of Saint Francis,
                 Rochester, MN.

Pages 46-47   Sister Generose Gervais, O.S.F., recalls a story (undocumented) about
                 the contractor, J. D. Billingsley, who fled Rochester without finishing

Saint Marys Hospital. Found hiding from the law in Texas, Billingsley was brought back to Rochester and tried; as part of his sentence, he performed menial construction work for a period of time without pay.

Pages 46-47   **Saint Marys Hospital Annals.**

Pages 48-49   **Clapesattle H: *The Doctors Mayo*, pp 250-252.**
Newspaper accounts describing hospital construction.

Page 49   **Clapesattle (p 252).**

Page 49   Mother Alfred is presumed to have named the hospital, but there is no documentation. For Catholics, naming the hospital "Saint Marys" put patients and staff under the protection of Mary, the mother of Jesus. The name "Saint Mary's" is commonly used for hospitals and other Catholic institutions. For example, the congregation would have called its college "Saint Mary's" if Bishop Patrick Heffron of Winona had not claimed it for his college, now called "Saint Mary's University of Minnesota."

Page 50   **Hayes MFA: *Years of Beginning, A History of the sisters of the Third Order Regular of Saint Francis of the Congregation of Our Lady of Lourdes*, p 44.**
"Some of the sisters complained to the bishop about Mother Alfred and her regime, for while Mother Alfred had been in the midst of every project, the burdens had become too heavy for some of the pioneer group."

Pages 50-52   *Mother Alfred as Superior: The Closing Years of Her Life*, **Saint Marys Hospital Annals, pp 22-25.**

Kraman C: *Odyssey in Faith: The Story of Mother Alfred Moes*, pp 194-197.

This period of Mother Alfred's life is described.

Page 51   *A Century of Caring: 1889-1989.* **Rochester, MN: Saint Marys Hospital, 1988, p 20.**
Mother Alfred's relationship with Mother Matilda and her work as the first hospital superintendent are noted in the text commemorating Saint Marys Hospital's centennial.

Pages 51-52   **Hayes (p 77).**
Sister Gabriel Hochgesung, housekeeper in the convent where Mother

Alfred spent her last years, dictated this account.

Page 52   Excerpts from the eulogy are reported in a letter from Mother Angela
                 Rosenberger of Joliet, Illinois. Undated. Congregational Archives,
                 Sisters of Saint Francis, Rochester, MN.

Kraman C: *Odyssey in Faith: The Story of Mother Alfred Moes*, p 214.

CHAPTER 4

Forging the Partnership

S aint Marys Hospital opened unpretentiously on September 30, 1889. The event, for the Franciscan Sisters and the Doctors Mayo, was secondary to the needs of patients they served. The Sisters adjusted the scheduled date and opened early because a patient required an eye procedure and the operating room was ready. The press, however, hailed the new institution with far more fanfare. Within the opening week, local newspapers ran several articles about the hospital, all of them enthusiastic and positive, if not completely accurate. In St. Paul, Archbishop John Ireland, in his archdiocesan newspaper, *The Northwest Chronicle*, praised the Sisters and Dr. William Worrall Mayo for their accomplishment: "St. Mary's Hospital in charge of the Sisters of St. Francis opened last week under very favorable auspices. Already eleven patients are being cared for therein. Medical aid is being given by the well-known and able physician Dr. Mayo. Miss Edith Graham, of Chicago, a specialist in the art of nursing, will give the Sisters some valuable assistance in that difficult department. . . . The noble order that has erected the hospital is entitled to the gratitude of the public."

The story of the hospital's beginnings revolves around a few unknown women and men who built the foundation of an extraordinary institution. The cornerstone of the foundation was their shared commitment to serve suffering humanity. Such commitment inspired unstinting efforts, tapped creative resources, and transcended religious differences. They forged a permanent partnership and in the process overcame formidable obstacles—not the least of which being their lack of experience with hospitals and how they operated. The physicians, without internship experience, had no training in hospital practice. The Sisters, untrained as nurses, were less prepared than the physicians for hospital service.

57

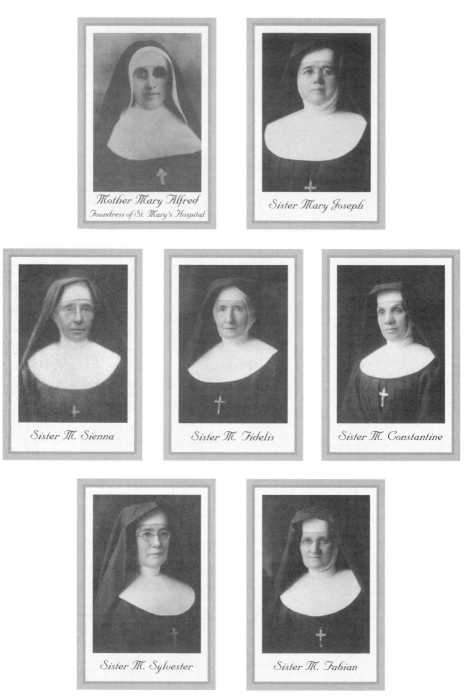

The pioneer Sisters of Saint Marys Hospital. (From Saint Marys Hospital Archives
and the Assisi Heights Archives, Rochester, MN.)

The physicians were the sons of Dr. W. W. Mayo, William J. (Will) and Charles H. (Charlie). At 28 years old, Dr. Will had practiced with his father for 6 years, and 24-year-old Dr. Charlie was a year out of medical school. Already Dr. Will showed outstanding ability in private practice, and Dr. Charlie demonstrated surgical ability equal to that of his brother. Dr. W. W. Mayo was now 70 years old and still commanded the confidence of patients. But he recognized that the "success in the new enterprise must rest upon the shoulders of the two younger Mayos. The father became consulting physician and surgeon, and they the attending staff."

The small group of Sisters at Saint Marys Hospital was four at first: Sisters Sienna Otto, Constantine Koupal, Fidelis Cashion, and Hyacinth Quinlan. Sister Joseph Dempsey joined them within a few weeks, followed by Sister Sylvester Burke in 1890 and by Sister Fabian Halloran, temporarily in 1890 and permanently in 1892. Biographer Helen Clapesattle describes them as sheltered, sensitive women "used to nothing more unnerving than

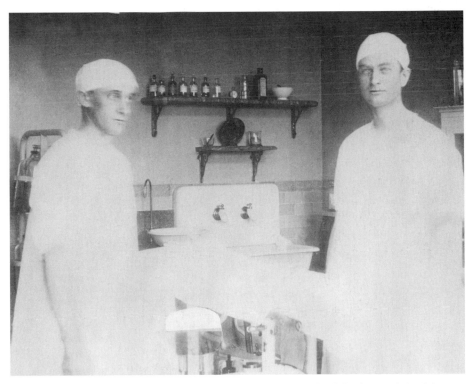

The young Doctors Mayo, Charles H. (left) and William J. (right). (From Saint Marys Hospital Archives.)

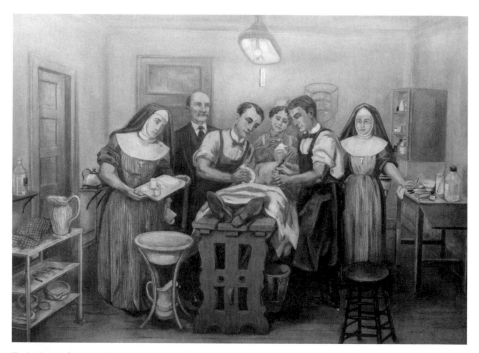

Painting of an early operation at Saint Marys Hospital. (From Saint Marys Hospital Archives.)

the pranks of children in the classroom, and for some of them the first operation they witnessed was a shock that remained a vivid memory for life." Edith Graham, associate of the Mayos who taught the Sisters the

rudiments of nursing, described one of Sister Joseph's first contacts with nursing: "She was asked to assist at the examination of a male patient whose ailment required that his entire body be uncovered for observation. While one of the doctors and Miss Graham worked with him, the young sister stood off in the corner, her back turned, quivering with outrage and shame. As she left the room when the task was done she protested vehemently to Miss Graham that she could never do such work, that she would ask Mother Matilda to send her back to teaching at once. But she stayed on, and quickly learned the lesson that the needs

Sister Joseph Dempsey, 1890. (From Saint Marys Hospital Archives.)

of human suffering transcend the dictates of modesty. In her subsequent management of Saint Mary's she was always on guard against prudery among the sisters, where it might lead to neglect in nursing."

Sister Joseph was Mother Alfred Moes' choice for head nurse and hospital administrator. At 33 years old, Sister Joseph had demonstrated her considerable abilities as teacher and principal of congregational schools. She was a Rochester native, and having a hometown girl heading the new hospital seemed an added advantage. As noted earlier, the other Sisters whom Mother Alfred chose for Saint Marys Hospital came from farms and towns across the Midwest. Sisters Sienna and Fabian were 21 years old, Sister Sylvester 26, and Sisters Constantine and Fidelis both 34. Their backgrounds and educations varied, but common for all was the frontier experience of hard work and resourcefulness. They also shared a religious commitment in that each had chosen to dedicate her life as a vowed Franciscan woman. As postulants and novices, their training was rigorous and disciplined. Those who persevered and received their superiors' approval made vows of poverty, chastity, and obedience. The vows and the Franciscan Rule would frame their lives. Prayer and sacrifice were guiding principles "in the spirit of Saint Francis, for the glory of God and the service of others." These Franciscan women ardently desired to serve with generosity that knew no boundaries and with humility that shunned personal recognition.

Except for Sister Hyacinth, who served as temporary administrator, Edith Graham taught nursing to all the Sisters for a few weeks in small, informal classes. Nursing as a profession was in an early, developmental stage. Routine duties included many housekeeping tasks, along with preparing and serving meals. Keeping the patients comfortable, dressing wounds, and giving medications were of foremost importance. The Sisters' training also included such technical

Edith Graham (later the wife of Dr. Charles H. Mayo). (From Saint Marys Hospital Archives.)

skills as using a thermometer, giving enemas, and inserting catheters.

Doctors Will and Charlie were well grounded in their medical profession when the hospital opened. Indeed, their father's medical guidance and encouragement began in boyhood. As Will put it, "We were reared in medicine as a farmer boy is reared in farming." They drove with their father on distant house calls and went to the bedside with him. They helped with operations and with autopsies, and for a time both boys worked in the local drugstore. Will and Charlie knew the art of medicine long before they received any formal instruction in its science. From early childhood, their parents, Louise and William Worrall Mayo, instilled strong social and ethical values in them. The Mayo boys grew up in a period of depression and hard times. Although not affluent, the family was better off than most of the neighbors. Many of the pioneers who settled the Minnesota frontier to find a better life faced drought, debt, bad crops, low prices, and lost homes. Will and Charlie saw the situation and its causes through their father's eyes, and learned the principle of noblesse oblige: "Our father believed that a man with unusual physical strength or with unusual intellectual capacity or opportunities owed something to the people. He should do for others in proportion as he had the strength to do."

As adults, the Mayo brothers spoke with awe about their mother's tolerance, understanding, and charitable spirit. "She accepted what there was in folks and did not criticize the bad. I never knew her to say a hateful word about anyone," recalled Dr. Will. At a later time, when a group of Rochester citizens gathered to honor Dr. Charlie, he told them, "The biggest thing Will and I ever did was to pick the father and mother we had." The partnership of the young Mayos and the Sisters at Saint Marys Hospital began tentatively. Indeed, at first glance, they appeared to have little in common. The Mayos were Protestant and, even in the small community of Rochester, of a different social status from the Sisters. The young men may have found the life of religious Sisters admirable, but it was clearly outside their experience. Their father's friendship with Mother Alfred and local priests made the Catholic religion less foreign and forbidding for them. The young men knew Father Thomas O'Gorman and recalled stories about him and their father doing house calls in the country. It was Father O'Gorman whom Dr. W. W. Mayo consulted about the choice of medical schools for his sons and who was a likely influence in Dr. Mayo's decision to send Dr. Charlie to Europe after medical school. Despite the diversity of their backgrounds, such mutual associations significantly helped the Mayos and the Franciscans bridge their differences. Most importantly, they shared an overriding common goal, the hospital's success.

Central to the challenges faced by the Sisters was a lack of funds. The congregation's leadership refused additional moneys and also denied requests for furniture from the motherhouse. Presumably, such a stance demonstrated the continued influence of Sisters who opposed the hospital and preferred that congregational assets go to educational works. Mother Alfred advertised in the newspapers, asking the public to furnish hospital rooms—such an approach had worked well for the Sisters of Charity when she was in Milwaukee. The only response received in Rochester, however, was a gift of books by Mr. Blakeley, the editor of *The Record and Union*.

The Sisters were responsible for furnishing the wards and private rooms, "and they were hard put to find the bare necessities." They opened only three small wards and one private room initially because they had barely a dozen iron cots, a few dozen unbleached muslin sheets and pillowcases, and some rough gowns. Outer bedclothing was scarce: "not the least task in preparing for the patient was to find covering for the bed." Someone donated a few heavy quilts of garish patterns, but there were no blankets until the hospital earned funds to purchase them. The mattresses did not fit the cots and slipped around on the crude springs; the nurses had to be alert to prevent them from sliding to the floor, carrying patient and bedclothing with them. Eight patients were admitted the first week and exhausted the number of beds set aside for patients. The Sisters gave up their own beds to make room for more patients. At bedtime, they dragged out extra mattresses and made up sleeping accommodations on the floor. In truth, they had no furniture except beds, "not a commode or a dresser in the hospital except one heavy black walnut piece sent over from the motherhouse." The rough wooden stands that held the washbowls were fitted with oilcloth covers whose edges Mother Alfred herself had pinked. Odds and ends of dishes and linens went on trays at mealtimes; the knives and forks were heavy iron pieces that had to be scoured after each meal to keep them presentable.

The Mayos equipped the single operating room, located on the second floor. It was about 12 feet square, faced north and had a large bay window of plate glass, a smaller window on either side, and a skylight of heavy glass. As noted, Dr. Charlie had recently visited hospitals on the Continent to observe new developments in surgical procedures and practice. Using his considerable mechanical skills, Dr. Charlie fashioned some extra instruments and built operating tables like the ones he had seen in European hospitals:

"He padded the top and covered it with oilcloth, then
slanted three boards down-
ward on the sides to carry the
fluids into tin drain pans held
in position by stirrups at the
corners. With large 'percola-
tors' to hold the antiseptic
solutions, plenty of tin basins
in which to rinse instruments
and sponges, and an array of
syringes for squirting boiled
water all around, the room
was ready for the wet operations then in vogue."

*The first operating table used at Saint Marys
Hospital, designed by Dr. Charles H. Mayo. (From
Saint Marys Hospital Archives.)*

Two years later, as a gift to Saint Marys Hospital, the Mayos bought a
complete set of operating room equipment in glazed enamelware manufactured in Berlin. They brought it from the World's Fair in Chicago.

Because there was no gas as yet in the pretty gas fixtures, the Sisters carried lanterns to light their way through the hospital at night. They hung a
lantern on a tree outside to guide the physicians and others coming to the
hospital after dark. An elevator shaft had been constructed through the
center of the building, but it had no elevator and no protective railing. Sister
De Paul Rein came from the motherhouse to sit guard in the evenings until
a railing could be built.

Contrary to the elaborate newspaper descriptions, the new hospital had
a modest interior. The first floor housed the Sisters' residence, offices, and
kitchen; on the second floor were the operating room, the women's 10-bed
ward, and two private rooms; and on the third floor were the chapel, two
wards for men, and two private rooms. The stairway went through the
center of the building. The kitchen's dumbwaiter on the first floor did not
work most of the time, so the Sisters carried the patients' meals to the upper
floors. All the water for the building had to be pumped by hand from a
basement reservoir that was replenished by a surface pipe connected with
the city water tank. The Sisters carried all the water used for cooking, baths,
and other purposes from the basement to the upper floors. A surface sewer
in the yard behind the hospital took care of sewage, except when it backed
up, as it did all too frequently. "Then the odor summoned the sisters by

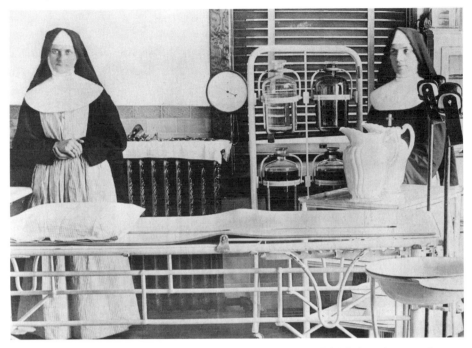

Sister Fabian Halloran (left) and Sister Constantine Koupal (right) at the second operating table (manufactured in Germany) to be used at Saint Marys Hospital. (From Saint Marys Hospital Archives.)

day or night to come and clean up the mess, and for the next few days, until the cesspool could be put in order again, the long-suffering nuns carried out all the slops." The hospital was not connected to the city sewer system until 1898—at the Sisters' expense.

The location of the hospital was more inconvenient than Mother Alfred had anticipated. Zumbro Street (now Second Street Southwest) was a country road, ungraded, unpaved, and without bordering sidewalks. Visitors and patients with no transportation trudged a mile through the woods from town on a footpath. Shortly after the hospital opened, Mother Matilda Wagner got lost in the woods on her way to Saint Marys when she took a cow path and the trail gave out. Every day, usually after supper, two of the Sisters walked to the shops on Broadway, where they purchased food for the next day and carried their parcels home. The distance to town was particularly difficult on Sundays, when they wished to attend Mass at St. John's. They intended that half of them would attend the 8 o'clock service and the remainder would go to the later Mass. Patients' needs, however, frequently did not fit the proposed schedule and the pastor added to the problem: "dear kindly Father Riordan was rather indifferent about the exact time for beginning Mass. Sometimes he was as much as an hour late and at other times he was nearly as much ahead of the hour assigned."

Regular duties demanded a rigorous schedule for the Sisters that began at 3:00 or 4:00 a.m. and ended at 11:00 or 12:00 p.m.: "To do the laundry work they used to rise at two or three o'clock in the morning and have it out of the way before the other work began. Operating room linen had to be washed, dried, and ironed in the evening after supper so that it would be ready for use the next day. . . . If a special nurse were needed at night, a Sister stayed up and remained on duty until the next night. Two days and the intervening night was not an unusual period on duty. . . . Their duty was to alleviate human suffering and to save human lives, and they did it."

Entirely without outside help, except for sporadic assistance from some itinerant janitor, "whose incompetence was endured only because he worked for a pittance," the Sisters carried an incredible load. As the numbers of patients increased, they repeatedly asked the motherhouse for more help, with no success. In desperation, Sister Hyacinth tried the unconventional practice of hiring lay help; she searched out two likely girls, Mary and Teresa, to work as maids "at $6.00 for the first month and $7.00 a month thereafter." The Mayos helped, too. For the first 3 years, there was no male orderly and the Mayo brothers added to their heavy practice the responsibility of nursing male patients who needed special attention. They took turns on night duty, "depending on the alarm clock to arouse them from sleep they dared not entirely forego."

The hospital had no telephone. When an emergency occurred and the Sisters needed the physicians, one of them left her work and carried the message on foot downtown to the Mayo office or home. To address the problem, they requested the city to set up telephone poles along Zumbro Street from the Mayo office to the hospital. Dr. Charlie, with his interest in new mechanics, installed the telephone with the aid of a neighbor boy. He and the same boy also installed the Mayos' Christmas gift to the hospital— an electric announcing system that allowed patients to call for nurses. As the story goes, these amateur electricians got some wires crossed, and "the bells would start ringing and would not stop." The Sisters carried shears with them as a precaution. "If a bell kept on ringing, swsshsh!! would go the wires, and next morning Dr. Charlie would have to resurrect the whole system again."

About the same time, the shaft was finally fitted with an elevator, thanks to a hobo and Dr. Charlie. The Sisters often fed hobos who came to the hospital door. After a good meal, one well-traveled guest told them about a hydraulic elevator he had seen in Paris. When Dr. Charlie learned about the invention, he decided to build one for the hospital. He and Fred Livermore, a local machinist, dug a 40-foot hole themselves and lowered several sections of pipe into it. When water from the basement reservoir rushed into the pipe, it pushed the elevator upward like a giant syringe. Dr. Charlie's biographer notes, "the thrifty Dr. Charlie could not bear to see the water wasted after each trip, so he ran a pipe up along one corner of the shaft into a tank on the roof. Then as the elevator descended it pumped the water up into the tank, from which it was piped into the toilets." The elevator, however, had at least one problem: it could be operated only from the inside. If it was on the third floor and needed on the first, "someone had to march up the stairs and go after the elevator."

Under such circumstances, it was indeed "worthy of awe," as one newspaper noted early in 1892, "that in a succession of four hundred admissions to Saint Mary's Hospital there were but two deaths." With characteristic magnanimity, the Mayos gave the Sisters all the credit for the hospital's success—". . . by unceasing toil, by determination to make good, by willingness to offer whatever sacrifice the task demanded." To all their labors, the Sisters added prayer: "Often while they worked lighted candles in their chapel kept vigil for them. When a critical operation had to be done they sent word to the convent for prayers, and many a rosary was said to bless the surgeon's work while he was operating. The Drs. Mayo did not share the sisters' faith, but they did not scorn it. One time when Dr. Will was leaving a seemingly hopeless case, he said to Sister Joseph, 'I know she can't live, but you burn the candles and I'll pay for them.'" The patient lived and got well.

High spirits and great resolve to overcome obstacles characterized the Franciscans and the young physicians. Anti-Catholicism, however, was an obstacle they could not overcome. Saint Marys Hospital opened to serve all sick persons regardless of their color, sex, financial status, or professed religion. Mother Alfred had put it clearly, "The cause of suffering humanity knows no religion and no sex; the charity of the Sisters of St. Francis is as broad as their religion." From the beginning, Mother Alfred asked Dr. W. W. Mayo to take charge of the new venture and, along with his sons, plan the hospital's construction. Although Mother Alfred recognized that Dr.

W. W. Mayo stood well above any Rochester physician, she had no intention of excluding other physicians from practicing at the hospital. All public announcements stated that patients could choose any physician they wished and that the hospital doors were "open to all physicians who wish to put their patients in the institution."

Dr. W. W. Mayo tried to organize a staff, but met with evasion and outright refusal. The physicians he approached were personally friendly, but they wanted no part of a venture that was sure to fail because of increasing anti-Catholicism. Between 1860 and 1890, the Catholic population in the United States tripled and continued to grow. Such waves of immigration alarmed native-born Protestants, who demanded curbs on Catholic voting, citizenship, and education. Increasing immigration was causing a resurgence of nativism in the United States, especially in the Middle West. The American Protective Association, successor to the Know-Nothings, forerunner of the Ku Klux Klan, and the most rabid anti-Catholic movement in the history of the nation, had been organized in Clinton, Iowa, in 1887 and had spread into States immediately north and east. Because the American Protective Association was reputedly strong in Minnesota, the Mayos ascribed much of the early opposition to Saint Marys Hospital to its influence. "Ardent Protestants would have none of an institution that was managed by black-robed nuns and in which there was a chapel set aside for the exercises of popery. . . ."

Out of concern for this threat to the success of Saint Marys Hospital, Dr. W. W. Mayo asked John Willis Baer, a prominent member of the Presbyterian Church, to become nominal superintendent of the hospital with the hope of overcoming Protestant prejudice. Goodnaturedly, Mr. Baer agreed to Dr. Mayo's requests and "for some weeks made frequent and ostentatious visits of inspection to the hospital—ostentatious until he got inside, where he became very unobtrusive indeed." The effort, which brought no Rochester physicians to the hospital, succeeded in aggravating some local Catholics. A vocal group already disagreed with the Sisters' choice of a non-Catholic physician to manage the hospital. These grievances were soon resolved, thanks to the Catholic bishop in Winona. Shortly after the hospital opened, Archbishop John Ireland established the new Diocese of Winona and named Joseph B. Cotter as Winona's first bishop. "A man of great wisdom and tact," Bishop Cotter's influence assured support for Saint Marys Hospital from the Catholic community. For a time Protestant objections to the hospital subsided and Rochester physicians began using Saint Marys Hospital. Friends of the hospital sponsored a public ball and contributed $70.00. In August 1890, Olmsted County commissioners began an annual contribution to the hospital for the care of their wards, and Rochester's three Masonic lodges paid $150.00 a year to maintain a free hospital bed for their members.

Just when external problems appeared to lessen, troubling practices within the hospital began to surface. Some Rochester physicians began to use Saint Marys Hospital ". . . as a pesthouse upon which to dump the heavy and dangerous care of infectious diseases." For these physicians, hospitalization was the last resort for terminally ill patients. The exemplary mortality rate at the hospital began to increase, to the alarm of the Sisters and the Mayos. They recognized that this practice, if continued, would jeopardize the reputation of the hospital. The Sisters took a bold step and ruled that no patient could be admitted without examination by one of the Mayos. The purpose of the ruling was to protect the hospital from abuse; the effect was to close the hospital to all but the Mayos and physicians who were willing to refer patients to them.

In initiating this policy, the Sisters demonstrated confidence and determination to provide for Saint Marys' successful future. Growing numbers of patient admissions substantiated such confidence. From September 30, 1889, to January 1, 1893, 1,037 patients were admitted and the number of deaths was 22. The death rate from 1889 to 1893 was as low as at any time in the hospital's history. Patients who heard of marvelous medical results in Rochester came from states across the country, from New York in the east to Montana in the west. They went home cured and, in turn, told others about their experience. At a time when the public shunned hospitals, the low mortality rate figured importantly in building respect for the institution and recognition for the extraordinary abilities of the Doctors Mayo.

Importantly, the hospital was paying its own way. Rates in the first year were a competitive $1.00 a day or $6.00 a week for ward beds and from $8.00 to $10.00 a week for private rooms: "The receipts for the first eleven months were about eleven hundred dollars." Careful stewards of their money, the Sisters used extra earnings to invest in the hospital; their first priority was making hospital rooms more inviting and homelike. They purchased good beds and bedclothing, rocking chairs, dressers, pictures, and mirrors. Attractive new dishes for patient dinner trays were a welcome addition, as were "the first half-dozen silver knives and forks . . . wrapped up between meals for better care." The 1890 hospital annals record that they also acquired transportation: "June 6 Purchase of a horse,

Sister Walburga Kukulska with a young patient. (From Saint Marys Hospital Archives.)

$100; Harness, $31.50; and buggy, $20. The 'buggy' was a second-hand delivery wagon; it had a canopy top, a cover held up by four rods, one at each corner. Mother Alfred with her usual enthusiasm called it a top buggy; otherwise it was known as the light wagon."

Beyond the purchase of material goods, the Sisters began their practice of investing in education for the staff. In March 1891, "Sister Joseph and Sister Constantine went for a period of observation and study at hospitals in St. Paul, Minneapolis, St. Joseph, Minnesota, and Chicago."

The Mayos, particularly Dr. Will, were relieved that the hospital was paying its own way. They did not believe the Franciscan congregation would make up any deficit, and this left them with full financial responsibility. They wanted the hospital to become fully self-supporting and even asked the Sisters not to set out boxes for donations to the poor. In their view, Saint Marys Hospital should earn money for its own charities, as they did, and finance its own improvements. The Mayos adopted the policy of telling patients to pay the Sisters' bill first and their bill for professional services second. The hospital's unprecedented growth, heralded on the one hand, presented serious problems on the other hand.

The Franciscan Sisters became acutely aware of such problems at one of the regular meetings of their governing board. At the July 1892 meeting of the Board of Trustees, Mother Matilda read a letter from the Doctors Mayo. They requested an addition to the hospital and listed their reasons: "Under the existing conditions (1) proper care was impossible because of overcrowding, (2) there were an insufficient number of private rooms, (3) a waiting list existed, and (4) there were inadequate provisions made for the sisters. With such an addition, a resident physician might be installed and a small training school for nurses be established."

The Mayos' letter also made specific suggestions for construction of the addition to meet the described needs. The Trustees asked Mother Matilda, Sister Joseph, and Sister Aquin Glockner to study the request and make a recommendation. In September, the Board approved the Mayos' request and appointed Sisters Joseph and Aquin "to secure plans and specification in accordance with those suggested by the doctors." Later, in the hospital annals, Sister Joseph made an intriguing comment on the proposed addition: "With the encouragement of the Doctors Mayo and the Right Reverend Bishop Cotter, the Sisters timidly ventured to erect a small addition accommodating about thirty beds." Her words "timidly ventured" indicate some hesitation over the addition; perhaps it was a question of filling the additional 30 beds or perhaps it was a concern about greater demands on an overworked staff of Sisters. Nevertheless, the project went forward: C. G. Maybury & Son of Winona was chosen as the architectural firm, and contracts were let on June 7, 1893, at a total cost of $17,338.95. While the Mayos and the Sisters planned the hospital addition, a significant obstacle from a new quarter presented itself, with far-reaching consequences.

W. A. Allen, M.D., the Mayos' homeopathic rival in Rochester, saw the advantage that Saint Marys Hospital gave his competitors and began making plans for a hospital of his own. He formed a partnership with another homeopath physician, hired a trained nurse, and rented a remodeled house. The new institution, Riverside Hospital, opened for patients in November 1892. At the same time, nativism again swept through the country in response to another unprecedented peak in Catholic immigration. Sentiment rose high enough to put American Protective Association planks against Catholic institutions in state political platforms. Local Protestants renewed their "opposition to Saint Mary's Hospital and pointed to the rival Riverside [Hospital] as an institution that Protestants and patriots could enter without doing outrage to their convictions by furthering an agency of the hated and alien Catholic Church." Dr. Allen saw his chance and made a bid for more business by inviting local physicians who were not homeopaths to use the Riverside Hospital.

At this juncture, two important members of the Presbyterian Church fell ill and were taken to Riverside Hospital; they called on the Doctors Mayo to attend them. The Mayos faced an important decision. On the one hand, to refuse to attend patients at Riverside Hospital cemented their alliance with the Catholic Saint Marys Hospital and made them a target of abuse by their fellow Protestants. On the other hand, to accept patients at Riverside divided their practice between two institutions and would have disastrous consequences for Saint Marys because most of their patients would choose the non-Catholic hospital. After deliberating, the Mayos refused to attend patients or to operate in the Riverside Hospital. Biographer Clapesattle assesses their decision: ". . . the Mayos were wise enough to see the advantages of centralizing their practice in one hospital under one staff—particularly a hospital and staff they controlled. . . . Moreover, the Mayos felt a strong moral obligation to the Sisters of St. Francis, who had just lately decided to put all their eggs in the Mayo basket and were even now adding to their investment. To divert a share, perhaps in time the larger share, of their practice to another hospital seemed wrong, a poor return for loyalty and confidence. And finally, the Mayos were not men inclined to knuckle under to public clamor or the pressure of opposition."

As anticipated, the Mayos' decision brought highly emotional censure and criticism from a segment of the Protestant community. From the pulpit, one enraged pastor called them servants of the Catholics and accused them of forgetting their sworn duty to the sick. Many took up the Riverside Hospital cause and helped the hospital through generous financial donations and volunteer programs; the press gave their efforts extensive coverage. Local citizens even elected Dr. Allen as mayor of Rochester. In the midst of these contentious times, the Mayos quietly focused on their practice and cared for patients. When critics attacked them and waited for a response, they chose to ignore the abuse and appeared unperturbed by it. Indeed, during the height of the controversy, Dr. Charlie married Miss Edith Graham on April 5, 1893. Assuredly, the new Mrs. Mayo had no difficulty supporting a position that favored her former pupils.

The Riverside Hospital was in operation for more than 2 years, when, in September 1895, Dr. Allen made a startling announcement. For unknown reasons, "at a peak of prosperity and popularity," and still mayor of Rochester, he was leaving his practice in Rochester and moving to St. Paul. Shortly after he left, Riverside Hospital closed and sold its beds and other movables to Saint Marys. Dr. Allen returned to Rochester the next year and carried on a large practice for many years, but he never reopened the Riverside Hospital. The hospital annals give only a summary note about Riverside Hospital and have no indication of the Sisters' response to events that threatened Saint Marys. Presumably, it was an extraordinarily difficult time for them, particularly because they were powerless to do anything about pervasive anti-Catholicism. They loved Saint Marys, rejoiced in their call to serve the sick, and wanted their institution to succeed. But in truth, they believed the success of the hospital was not up to them, but was in God's hands. And so, as was their custom in times of difficulty and decision, they fasted and prayed that God would bless the work of their hands.

Undoubtedly, the Sisters were grateful for the unexpected departure of Dr. Allen and the subsequent closing of Riverside Hospital. Their overwhelming gratitude and admiration, however, went to the Mayos. They would never forget how the Mayos endured public abuse with steadfast courage on their behalf; the Mayos' unswerving loyalty had almost certainly saved the hospital. All of the Rochester Franciscans, those who favored the hospital and those less enthusiastic, applauded the Mayos, whose stance during these difficult times helped the congregation set aside whatever reservations they had and recognize Saint Marys Hospital as a worthy Franciscan institution.

The strident competition over Riverside Hospital cemented the relationship between the Doctors Mayo and the Sisters at Saint Marys Hospital. Despite inexperience, hardship, and hostility, they had learned to depend on each other. The Mayos, forced by circumstances, found they could furnish all the patients needed for the hospital. In turn, the Sisters demonstrated they could provide all the physicians needed in a hospital and nursing care. Each made the decision to rely solely on the other. The Mayos' decision centralized their surgical practice and became a primary factor in their phenomenal success. The Sisters' decision moved Saint Marys Hospital beyond perceived parochial boundaries and into the mainstream of America.

ENDNOTES

Page 57   *Northwest Chronicle.* **October 11, 1889. Archives of the Archdiocese of Minneapolis and St. Paul.**

Page 59   **Clapesattle H:** *The Doctors Mayo.* **Minneapolis: The University of Minnesota Press, 1941, p 256.**
The Doctors Mayo and the Sisters in new roles.

Page 62   **Clapesattle** describes Doctors William J. and Charles H. Mayo's moral and professional development **(pp 177-180)**. "The Old Doctor asked Father O'Gorman's advice about training his sons for medicine. . . ." **(p 181)**.

Page 63   *Record and Union.* **October 25, 1889, p 3.**
"Sisters of St. Francis thank Mr. A. W. Blakeley for the books he donated to the hospital."

Pages 63-66   **Saint Marys Hospital Annals, pp 26-30.**

             Clapesattle (pp 257-263).

Sources for the beginnings of Saint Marys Hospital.

Page 66   **Saint Marys Hospital Archives.**
"Elevator," a dictated note by Sister Sylvester Burke to Sister Mary Brigh Cassidy, gives a firsthand account.

Page 67   **Saint Marys Hospital Annals, 1892.**

             Clapesattle (pp 260-261; n. 762).

Story of the candles and Dr. William J. Mayo's remarks.

Page 68   **Clapesattle (pp 253-254).**

             A Souvenir of Saint Mary's Hospital, **pp 15-16.**

Dr. W. W. Mayo's attempt to recruit doctors, the response of the American Protective Association, and Mr. Baer's role.

Rochester Post, **July 5, 1889, 3, c 3.**
". . . hospital arrangement under direction of Dr. W. W. Mayo, but open

to all doctors who wish to put in their patients."

Page 69   **Clapesattle H:** *The Doctors Mayo*, **p 264.**
"No patient should be admitted to St. Mary's Hospital until he had been examined by one of the Drs. Mayo."

Pages 69-70   **Saint Marys Hospital Annals.**
Financial data and hospital purchases noted in 1890.

Page 71   Letter dated July 20, 1892, from Doctors W. W. Mayo, A. W. Stinchfield, W. J. Mayo, and C. H. Mayo to Sisters of Saint Francis, Board of Trustees. Congregational Archives of the Sisters of Saint Francis, Assisi Heights, Rochester, MN.

Pages 71-73   **Clapesattle (pp 264-267, 763).**

                    Saint Marys Hospital Annals, 1892.

                    Story of Dr. W. A. Allen and the Riverside Hospital and bibliographic note.

CHAPTER 5

Pioneers in Surgery

T wo events serve as bookends for this chapter on 28 years of the Sisters' Story, from 1894 to 1922. They are the recorded dedication speeches for the hospital's first and sixth additions. During this period, Saint Marys Hospital added six buildings to its original structure. The institution was in constant change as the Sisters tried to keep pace with increasing numbers of patients and expanding services. The first addition increased the bed capacity by 30, but in a short time the hospital was over-crowded: "As the annual number of patients edged toward one thousand, Saint Marys opened a second addition in 1898, a third in 1904, and a fourth in 1909. The latter included laboratories, a third operating room, and a maternity ward. . . . The fifth addition was finished three years later, and it raised the capacity of the hospital to three hundred beds and six operating rooms. By 1914, twenty-five years after its opening, Saint Marys Hospital was treating nearly eight thousand inpatients per year and nearly two thousand outpatients."

The dedication ceremonies of April 4, 1894, give a glimpse of the human story behind such remarkable growth. At the same time that Saint Marys dedicated its first addition, Riverside Hospital, supported by a vocal anti-Catholic segment, was "at the peak of its popularity and prosperity." Moreover, the Mayos, having refused to practice at Riverside Hospital, were publicly out of favor with that group. Neither competition at the doorstep nor public condemnation appeared to dampen the enthusiasm of the Franciscan Sisters and the Mayos for opening the new addition. The day of dedication, however, did not begin well. Bishop Joseph Cotter, host of the event, telegraphed from Winona that he was ill, but "would come on the afternoon train if he were able." At 3 o'clock, the bishop, only partially recovered, arrived for the public reception. About 800 persons, invited through the local papers, came for the occasion. Dr. William J. Mayo and Father William Riordan introduced each guest to Bishop Cotter, who was dressed in his episcopal robes. The receiving line clearly testified to Catholic endorsement and the Mayos' close affiliation with Saint Marys Hospital.

After the public reception, selected guests were invited to the mother-house, where the Sisters served a banquet. After the dinner, academy pupils gave a short program, followed by speeches. Chairman of the event, Dr. William Worrall Mayo, gave the Sisters a rousing tribute: "The building which we are met to dedicate represents the work of the Sisters of Saint Francis. The hospital has sprung up and developed into its present magnificent proportions almost without your knowing it. To many of our people it is as a grand and useful gift dropped from the clouds. It has cost you not one cent of money, not one hour of labor, not one moment of anxiety, and there it stands without a peer in the Northwest, one of the brightest ornaments of your fair city . . . surpassed by no hospital in the United States. The Sisters of Saint Francis have done this for us out of their goodness and charity, and I thank you in their name for your appreciation of their efforts."

With these remarks, Dr. W. W. Mayo began a family tradition of recognizing the Sisters of Saint Francis as solely responsible for the success of Saint Marys Hospital. Later that evening, Dr. William J. (Will) and Dr. Charles H. (Charlie) followed their father's example. Dr. Will put it succinctly: "All the credit for the successful treatment of patients at the hospital here, is due to the ministrations of the devoted, skillful Sisters in charge. We are but the Sisters' agents."

Dr. Charlie spoke next: "The success of our work is due to the sisters, to their constant skillful care for the patients at Saint Marys Hospital."

Throughout their lives, the Mayos gave the Sisters countless tributes. Not in 1894, nor at any time, did they refer to their own central, inestimable contribution to the institution. The relationship of the Doctors Mayo and the Sisters of Saint Francis was unique for its own time and beyond. Saint Marys was the only U.S. hospital owned by Catholic Sisters in an exclusive partnership with nonsectarian physicians. Perhaps even more unusual, a handshake sealed this partnership for almost 100 years. Based on trust and mutual respect, their pledge required no written documents or legal agreements.

That evening, Dr. W. W. Mayo, in great form, told his famous story about the origins of Saint Marys Hospital. He recalled the visit of Mother Alfred

William Worrall Mayo, M.D. (center), and his sons, Charles H., M.D. (left), and William J., M.D. (right), around 1900.

Moes to his office following the tornado of August 21, 1883. She informed him that Rochester needed a hospital; she promised that if he and his sons would staff a hospital, she and her Sisters would find the funds to build it. He described his efforts to dissuade her and how she convinced him. "She was, I think, a wonderful woman, so full of hope and energy."

The Honorable A. T. Stebbins, president of Rochester's Board of Trade, followed Dr. Mayo on the program, and extended his congratulations to the Sisters and Doctors Mayo for Saint Marys Hospital. Mr. Stebbins spoke again at the 1922 building dedication and admitted that he had not been as sanguine as he sounded that evening: "I remember the opening we had twenty-eight years ago. Some who were with me then are not here tonight. . . . Among ourselves we talked about various things and discussed the possibility of making a success of a hospital here in Rochester; we thought that the hospital as it was then was too large, that there would not be enough people coming here to keep it up, that it was too big for this small city. But look at the magnificent institution we are celebrating today! The best in the world! No place in the wide world has better facilities for caring for the sick."

With predictable hyperbole, other speakers assessed the accomplishments of Saint Marys Hospital and predicted future achievements. Not for some time, however, would any of them appreciate the singular factors that figured so importantly in the hospital's success.

Many years later, Dr. Will reflected that much of the success was due to the time at which he and his brother entered medicine. "Stress the unusual opportunity," he urged his biographer, "that existed in the time, the place, the general setup, not to be duplicated now." Dr. Will referred to surgical developments that yielded unprecedented opportunity. Indeed, Saint Marys Hospital had the good fortune of opening during a new surgical era. Infection was the surgeon's greatest nemesis. Even after successful surgical procedures, septic infections invaded the patient's wounds and caused high fever and, many times, death. In 1864, Scottish surgeon Joseph Lister demonstrated that bacterial microorganisms caused surgical infections and that antisepsis could kill them. Lister's technique, called wet antisepsis, used carbolic acid to bathe wounds, soak surgical dressings, and spray the air surrounding the patient during operation. Wherever surgeons practiced antisepsis, operations increased in volume and scope. Before Lister, a hospital of 200 or 300 beds might record 400 operations a year, 25% of them amputations. After Lister, a hospital of equal size could reasonably expect 4,000 or 5,000 operations a year, with less than 1% of them amputations.

Although wet antisepsis was highly effective, not a few physicians, including W. W. Mayo, objected to its messiness and the slippery floors it caused. Both Doctors Will and Charlie were introduced to the method in medical school and later viewed its effective use during tours of U.S. and European hospitals.

Dr. William J. (Will) Mayo.

When Saint Marys Hospital opened in 1889, they practiced wet antisepsis, and their father did not discourage them. As a result, patient death rates averaged 2.1%, an almost unheard-of rate, during the first 4 years. Within a few years, asepsis, designed to prevent wound infections before they began, replaced wet antisepsis. This practice introduced steam sterilization of surgical dressings and of clothing worn by surgeons and nurses at the operating table. Before the operation, surgical teams scrubbed hands and arms with soap and water, then soaked them in a solution of bichloride of mercury. They also sterilized the site of the surgical incision and used only sterilized surgical instruments and sutures.

Fired with ambition to create a surgical center on a level with hospitals of the eastern United States, the Mayos kept abreast of new developments. One at a time, over several years, they made extended visits to leading surgical centers in Baltimore, Boston, Philadelphia, and Chicago, where they observed the work of selected surgeons. "We were a green crew and we knew it," was Dr. Will's description of Saint Marys' first surgeons and nurses.

Yet, it was their acknowledged inadequacy and a consuming desire to overcome it that helped create the extraordinary team of Mayo surgeons and Sister-nurses. From the beginning, the Mayos were determined to bring back from every trip some specific improvement that could be applied in Rochester—even if it was only a new kind of soap or antiseptic. When one of them returned from a trip, Sister Joseph Dempsey would remark, "Now I wonder what new things we will need to do." The Sisters were as committed to improving in their areas of practice as the Mayos were in surgery.

In 1897, 8 years after Saint Marys Hospital opened, the Mayos performed 915 operations.

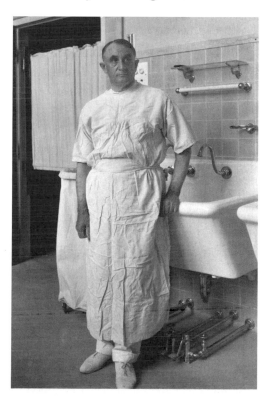

Dr. Charles H. (Charlie) Mayo.

The number grew to 1,823 by 1900, to 3,154 by 1903, and to more than 5,000 by 1906, and more than half of them were intra-abdominal. Working in their remote location without nearby competitors, the Mayos performed some operations by the hundreds or even by the thousands. The articles they contributed to medical journals, which described their successes in unprecedented numbers of cases, sent the Mayo Clinic soaring to world-wide prominence during the years 1895 to 1906.

At first the brothers operated together because they found their combined technical skills produced the best results. Working as a team, each took turns serving as the other's first assistant. Together they discussed every feature of their operations and pooled knowledge and ingenuity to meet a crisis when it came. The Mayos came to be viewed as almost a single medical entity. In appearance and manner, however, the brothers were quite opposite — Dr. Will was fair and blond, Dr. Charlie dark in skin and hair; Dr. Will was erect, compact, and commanding, Dr. Charlie more homey and comfortable-looking, never so precise or neat. Despite outward differences, their personal respect and commitment to each other was unshakable. When talking about themselves, they rarely used "I" or "me" but preferred to say "My brother and I." A colleague in later years remarked, "Your great success was not as surgeons. It was as brothers. There has never been anything like it."

Typically, the Sisters and Doctors Mayo talked over ideas and made decisions sitting around a kitchen table having a little refreshment. When Doctor Will or Charlie came back from one of their "brain-dusting tours," they gathered to discuss how a new idea might be implemented. One of the decisions they made was not to admit medical patients with conta-gious diseases lest they put surgical patients at risk. A few years later, they announced that the hospital was exclusively surgical. Their decision was entirely pragmatic. Hard pressed to find sufficient hospital beds for an increasing number of surgical patients, they would not treat medical patients at Saint Marys Hospital until adequate accommodations could be provid-ed. The cardinal principle was utmost simplicity consistent with good work; as Dr. Will put it, ". . . to get the patient well with as little loss of time as possible; whatever contributes to this end is adopted; whatever does not is eliminated."

As the Mayo brothers acquired prominence, a large number of surgeons, both national and international, came to Rochester: "They came to Rochester because they were fascinated by the fact that two young, unheralded surgeons, native sons of the Midwest, should have developed a center of surgery in an out-of-the-way village. The large number of patients operated upon daily permitted the demonstration of all the newer surgical procedures in the course of a few days. The visiting surgeons not only could witness the technical skill of the Drs. Mayo but they could hear them discuss surgical problems and experiences in their operating room. Their simple, informal remarks reflected the personalities of the Mayos themselves, who were frank, unassuming and honest men."

The Mayos' expanding surgical practice prompted them to ask other physicians to join them, particularly in the medical and laboratory areas. In 1893, they hired Augustus W. Stinchfield, M.D., a local physician of repute, and 3 years later, Christopher Graham, M.D., Edith Graham Mayo's able brother, joined the staff. For 25 years, Dr. Graham would serve as the hospital's attending physician. Esteemed confidant of the Sisters, Dr. Graham was inseparably linked with the history of Saint Marys: "His executive ability, his forceful personality, his prudence and foresight, were of incalculable value to the hospital and clinic especially during their formative period. . . . No staff member was oftener or more confidently quoted.

Visiting surgeons observe an operation being performed by Dr. William J. Mayo, assisted by Sister Joseph. (From Saint Marys Hospital Archives.)

Deservedly esteemed by his associates, his example was to them an inspiration and an incentive to the highest ideals of their calling."

By the turn of the century, the Mayo medical roster numbered eight doctors, among them the brilliant Henry S. Plummer, M.D., and Edward Starr Judd, M.D., a Rochester native, who became the first surgeon other than the Mayos to operate in Saint Marys Hospital. Pathologist Louis B. Wilson, M.D., joined the staff in 1905 and asked for a room adjacent to the operating rooms. Dr. Wilson made microscopic examinations of frozen sections of tissue for diagnosis. Two years later, William C. MacCarty, M.D., from Johns Hopkins, joined the staff and refined the diagnostic value of "living-tissue diagnosis." Dr. MacCarty was first in a generation of three MacCarty physicians to serve at Mayo. His son, Collin MacCarty, M.D., a neurosurgeon, recalled that his father made an important contribution beyond developing surgical pathology. He succeeded in attracting physicians from eastern medical schools, who did not know Mayo, to work with him in summer study groups. Some of the most gifted of them received appointments to the Mayo Clinic medical staff.

In the course of her work as surgical nurse, Sister Joseph acquired a taste for the operating room. Dr. Will recognized her unusual ability and chose her over a physician as his first assistant. They often worked before a gallery of visiting surgeons. Dr. Will would explain the procedure while Sister

Louis B. Wilson, M.D.

William C. MacCarty, M.D.

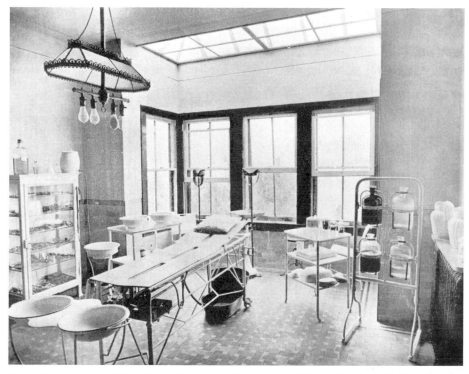

Operating room at Saint Marys Hospital. (From Saint Marys Hospital Archives.)

Joseph continued with the operation: "Her fingers flew like magic and often, before they knew it, the operation was over." On occasion, Dr. Will asked her to feel some obscure lesion to confirm or reject his own opinion. Indeed, Dr. Will later said of Sister Joseph, "Of all the splendid surgical assistants I have had, she easily ranks first." It was Sister Joseph who first called attention to an umbilical nodule, which is often the only physical indication of a particular form of abdominal cancer. "Sister Joseph's nodule" is the name surgical references now give for this condition. For 25 years, Sister Joseph spent her mornings across the operating table from Dr. Will. By 1915, however, increasing responsibilities as hospital superintendent required that she devote her time fully to administrative duties.

Sister Sylvester Burke was Dr. Will's choice for nursing supervisor, and she remained in that position until he stopped operating in July 1928. At the dedication ceremonies in 1922, Dr. Judd recognized the work of several Franciscan nurses and paid special tribute to Sister Sylvester: "One of the most wonderful of them all is Sister Sylvester who has been in the operating room since the hospital began and who is not only most proficient herself but has also trained many others to be excellent operating room assistants."

Sister Theodora Mikolai, one of the nurses trained by Sister Sylvester, was herself another legend in surgery. Her story is not unlike that of many young Sisters assigned to Saint Marys Hospital. When Sister Theodora went to Saint Marys in 1897, she first worked in the laundry with Sister Sarah Hoffmann, then on the patient floors, where she helped with cleaning. She learned the basics of nursing on the floors. She became a surgical nurse in 1907, and she

E. Starr Judd, M.D.

continued in that position for more than 50 years. Much later, she recalled those first years in the operating room: "We put in some long days. After surgery we always cleaned the operating rooms. Then in the afternoons we boiled surgical gloves, cut surgical sponges, and even made sutures from horsehair. I remember how Sister Joseph used to take hair from the

Sister Sylvester Burke.
(From Saint Marys Hospital
Archives.)

horses we had. We'd get enough to make a roll, and then we'd soak it in strong soap for a week before boiling it to be used in surgery."

Discipline and the ability to think clearly under pressure were particularly crucial for the surgical nurse. Failure to produce the right instrument at the proper moment, failure to follow directions exactly, failure to act coolly in an emergency—any of these actions might contribute to the death of the patient who lay on the operating table. Oliver H. Beahrs, M.D., first practiced surgery at Saint Marys and subsequently developed the department at Rochester Methodist Hospital. He emphasized the critical importance of teamwork in surgery and vividly recalled "two great team players at Saint Marys,"

Sister Paula Leopold and Doris Unland, a legendary supervisor of surgery.

Preparation for surgery was also important. Behind the scenes, a three-room unit on the third floor of the surgical pavilion was highly important. Called the Dressing Room, it was the precursor of what is now called Central Service. Sister Thomasine Drexler, "German and meticulously careful," supervised the preparation of surgical dressings and intravenous solutions. In the operating room itself, all instruments, sponges, and sutures had to be ready and in their proper places before a procedure began. Once the operation was under way, there was little time to find forgotten instruments, so the nurses kept precise notes as to which doctor used which tools. Sister William Fischenich, a surgical supervisor on Dr. Judd's service, seemed to model the necessary requisites of a good surgical nurse; she also had a

personality few on the surgical team would forget. One young surgeon, Gunther Nagel, M.D., wrote a book about training at Mayo Clinic and recalled his years in operating Room Five when Sister William ("Sister Bill") was in charge: "Sister Bill was a personality in her own right. She moved silently and rapidly about the room, or rather she seemed to glide without visible means of locomotion. . . . Her sharp, expressive eyes saw everything in the room at once. There was no dawdling in Room Five as it was being readied for the day's surgery. . . . While an operation was in progress, Sister Bill stood rigidly still by the instrument table, her eyes fixed on the operative field. Every step of the procedure was anticipated and the required instrument was in the surgeon's hand at

Doris Unland and Sister Paula Leopold, surgery supervisors. (From Saint Marys Hospital Archives.)

the exact instant it was needed. There was no need for words and hardly one was spoken. No wonder things went smoothly in Room Five! . . . The team functioned with the effortless grace of perfection—a surgeon's dream come true."

Dr. Nagel, afterward clinical professor of surgery at Stanford University, failed to mention Sister William's legendary love for Notre Dame football—perhaps out of loyalty to his Stanford team. The hospital annals of 1923 note a new postgraduate program in surgical nursing that Sister William helped establish: "To meet a demand for post-graduate training the school added a special course in surgical nursing and operating room work for registered nurses, graduates of reputable training schools. The course covers six months and in order that services can be properly rotated, only two applicants are received each month."

Supervisors in surgery, beginning with Sister William, wrote a text on the practice of surgery at Saint Marys School of Nursing. Entitled *The Operating Room: Instructions for Nurses and Assistants*, the text was first published in 1920. Five

Sister William Fischenich ("Sister Bill"). (From Nagel GW: The Mayo Legacy. Springfield, IL: Charles C Thomas, Publisher, 1966, p 76.)

editions followed, each one revised and expanded to include new surgical procedures. Detailed descriptions, accompanied by illustrations, followed each step of a surgical procedure. In addition, the text included illustrated directions for sterile procedures, arrangement of surgical instruments, and preparation of the patient. As supervisor of surgery, Sister Loretta Klinkhammer collaborated in writing text for the later editions; she recalled that many other persons, besides postgraduate nurses, used the texts. Physicians who completed their surgical fellowships and residencies at Mayo Clinic purchased them in large numbers. The text helped them initiate their staffs to the procedures they had learned at Mayo Clinic.

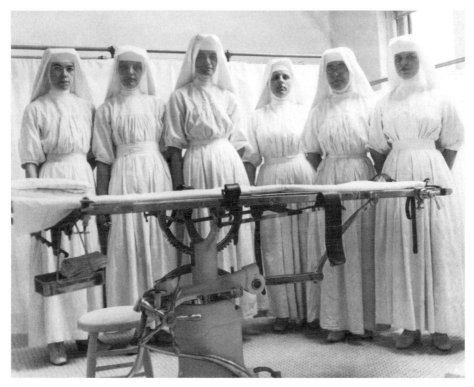

Operating room supervisors. Sisters (left to right) Lucille O'Donnell, Bertilla Lebens, William Fischenich, Theodora Mikolai, Sylvester Burke, Virginia Guiney. (From Saint Marys Hospital Archives.)

With the astonishing growth in surgery, the Mayos seemed to need a new addition before the last one was even completed. In 1905 when Doctors Will and Charlie pointed out the need for another addition, Sister Joseph told them she would pray about the matter that night. The next morning, she reported, "God did not approve of expansion just yet." Dr. Will replied, "That's odd, Charlie and I consulted God, too, and he told us to go ahead and build." Sister Joseph's authority prevailed at the time, but not for long. Rochester businessman John Kahler formed a company that responded to the space needs. Over the next years, Kahler built several small hotel-hospitals with a combined capacity of 300 beds and 5 operating rooms. The Mayos made no move to transfer their operating space from Saint Marys. The Sisters were not about to have the first hospital in Rochester relegated to secondary status and decided to end their halfway measures. They would no longer build additions that were overcrowded almost before the contractor finished but would build for the future. On October 2, 1919, they broke ground for a new surgical pavilion "with a view to use the other buildings for medical work." With consummate financial advice from Mother Matilda Wagner, Sister Joseph almost single-handedly planned the new building. The pavilion would cost $2,225,000 and double the hospital's capacity to 600 beds. Bishop Patrick Heffron of Winona, successor to Bishop Cotter, was foremost among those who encouraged the new building: "We have the best surgeons in the world, the best sisters in the world, and why can't we have the best hospital in the world?"

The new pavilion was dedicated on May 12, 1922, National Hospital Day. The overall context of the opening bore striking contrast to the dedication of the first addition in 1894. The Sisters sent 2,000 engraved invitations and had elegant souvenir books of Saint Marys Hospital printed for the occasion. Rochester papers announced that all businesses would be closed "so that employers and employees might have the time on that day to visit Saint Marys Hospital." The bus line altered service for the opening and made

The surgical pavilion, 1922. It is now called the Joseph Building. (From Saint Marys Hospital Archives.)

Saint Marys Hospital its terminal instead of the downtown area. Even the Twilight League of local baseball teams "decided to stage the scrap" a day early because of the event. A letter from the Sisters, carried in all Rochester papers, gave thanks for "cordial support and loyal cooperation that we have always received from the people of Rochester."

Four thousand guests attended the opening and toured a facility hailed as the most advanced of any hospital in the country. Designed in Renaissance style, the pavilion was seven stories high, the largest hospital structure ever built in Rochester. It included a pathology laboratory, x-ray facilities, classrooms, and the latest in dietary services and equipment, but the surgical suite was the highlight. Large windows with wrought iron railings framed the exterior of the surgical section. Inside, the suite contained ceilings that were two-stories high with 11 operating rooms. Ten of the operating rooms were of similar size, grouped in pairs, with gallery space for 30 physicians around the areas. The clinic amphitheater was in the center of the surgical wing and contained 200 seats in a semicircular bank for visiting physicians, nurses, and visitors.

After the public reception, Sister Joseph personally greeted the 500 guests who gathered for a banquet and then found a place for herself in a dark corner of the room. D. C. Balfour, M.D., chaired the formal presentations that followed the banquet. Bishop Heffron gave the opening speech and noted three things he believed characterized Saint Marys Hospital from its beginnings: "skillful medicine and surgery, sympathy for the patient, and *heart*." Twenty speakers followed the bishop and, although some exceeded their 2-minute limit, all gave sincere, frequently eloquent, tributes to the Sisters and the Doctors Mayo. As Rochester's *Daily Post and Record* noted, "Nearly all those who took part in the program emphasized not so much the monument of brick and stone represented by the new addition as the self-sacrifice of the Sisters of Saint Francis that made the building possible."

In his address, Dr. Louis B. Wilson, colleague of the Sisters for 17 years, mused about what might be "in the minds of the good Sisters this evening." He reminded them that with every new hospital building, they had wondered where they would find other women with the same spirit of kindness, who would take the same human interest in the individual patient that has always made Saint Marys more a home than a hospital. And now, he continued, with 300 more patients coming to fill the beds of this institution, you look for others with womanly kindness who will devote themselves, their lives, and their personal interests to the welfare of the individual patient: "I know you have faith that we can find them . . . for you have established this tradition firmly. It would be almost impossible to break it, and it is the greatest fact in our dealing with the sick who come to us, whether they be poor or wealthy, lowly or high in this world's esteem."

Dr. Will concluded the program and forcefully stated that a new building was not the only thing necessary: "What we accomplish in the future will not be due to the bricks and mortar, but to the soul and spirit that reside within Saint Marys Hospital."

Dr. Balfour then intimated to the guests that he had a rather difficult task ahead of him and needed their help. He called on Sister Joseph to speak, and with that the audience rose and applauded until she came forward from her dark corner of the room: "My very dear friends. I do not deserve the plaudits given me tonight, but I will take them to distribute them among the sisters with whom I have worked for so many years to make Saint Marys Hospital a house of God and a gateway to heaven for His many suffering children."

ENDNOTES

Page 77
: *A Century of Caring 1889-1989.* **Rochester, MN: Saint Marys Hospital, 1988, pp 29, 32.**
Summarized 1889-1914 hospital admissions and building additions.

Pages 77-80
: *Saint Marys Hospital Annals, 1894.*
Contains a complete description of the dedication ceremonies and speeches.

Page 79
: *Saint Marys Hospital Annals, 1922.*
Mr. A. T. Stebbins' speech.

Page 80
: **Clapesattle H:** *The Doctors Mayo.* **Minneapolis: The University of Minnesota Press, 1941, p 270.**
Refers to Dr. William J. Mayo's remarks.

Pages 80-81
: **Bordley J III, Harvey AM:** *Two Centuries of American Medicine: 1776-1976.* **Philadelphia: W. B. Saunders Company, 1976, pp 300-301.**
Description of the new era in surgery.

Pages 81-82
: **Clapesattle (pp 192-197, 273, 298-300, 358)** comments on the impact of the new surgical era on the Mayos' surgical practices.

Pages 81-82
: *Saint Marys Hospital Annals, 1897, 1903, 1906.*
Documents the surgical numbers.

Page 82
: **Clapesattle** describes the Mayo brothers and their relationship **(pp 300, 418, 671-673).**

Page 82
: **Clapesattle** comments on the relationship between the Sisters and the Mayos **(p 459).**

: *Saint Marys Hospital Archives.*
References on relationship.

Page 82
: *Twenty-fifth Annual Report of Saint Marys Hospital, Rochester, Minnesota: For the Year 1914,* **p 4.**
Notes that the hospital is exclusively surgical.

Pages 82-83
: **Braasch WF:** *Early Days at the Mayo Clinic.* **Springfield, IL: Charles C Thomas, Publisher, 1969, p 69.**
Colleague reflects on the Mayos' surgical prominence.

Pages 83-84   *A Souvenir of Saint Mary's Hospital: Founded in Eighteen Hundred and Eighty Nine*, **1922, p 59.**
Printed for the dedication of the surgical pavilion, contains a tribute to Dr. Christopher Graham.

Page 84   Interview with Dr. Collin S. MacCarty, October 17, 1998.

Pages 84-85   **Nagel GW:** *The Mayo Legacy.* **Springfield, IL: Charles C Thomas, Publisher, 1966.**
Dr. Gunther W. Nagel, who trained as a surgical fellow at Mayo Clinic, recalls his experience and describes Sister Joseph Dempsey's "exceptional ability."

Clapesattle H: *The Doctors Mayo,* **pp 370, 460.**

Page 85   **Bailey H:** *Demonstrations of Physical Signs in Clinical Surgery.* **11th ed. Baltimore: Williams & Wilkins Company, 1949, pp 227.**

Powell FC, Cooper AJ, Massa MC, Goellner JR, Su WP: Sister Mary Joseph's Nodule: A Clinical and Histologic Study. *J Am Acad Dermatol* **1984;10:610-615.**

Schwartz IS: Sister (Mary?) Joseph's Nodule. *N Engl J Med* **1987;316:1348-1349.**

Sister Joseph's nodule, nomenclature for carcinoma metastatic to the umbilicus. At the time Sister Joseph entered the congregation, every Sister received the name "Mary"; however, in most cases, it was not used in daily parlance.

Pages 85-86   **Saint Marys Hospital Annals, 1922.**
Dr. Edward Starr Judd's tribute to Sister Sylvester Burke.

Sister Mary Brigh: *Notes on Sister Sylvester.* **Saint Marys Hospital Annals, 1950.**

Pages 85-86   **Sister Sylvester:** *The Bartlett Method.* **Saint Marys Hospital Archives.**

Sister Sylvester: *Catgut Dry Method (or Boeckman).* **Saint Marys Hospital Archives.**
In the early 1950s Sister Sylvester wrote two accounts of sterilization methods used in surgery.

Page 86   *"Interview With Sister Theodora Mikolai,"* **June 1984. Saint Marys**

Hospital Archives.

"Memoirs of Sister Bertilla [Lebens] in the Operating Room With Dr. Charlie and Dr. Will Mayo: 1917-1940. **1969.**
The Archives also contains several additional interesting recollections and interviews of the early Sisters in surgery, among them: Sister Columba Michalak's recollections on her work with outpatients and in surgery support services.

Pages 86-87   Interview with Dr. Oliver H. Beahrs, October 13, 1998.

Pages 87-88   **Nagel GW:** *The Mayo Legacy,* **pp 76-79.**
Description of Sister William Fischenich.

Page 88   *The Operating Room: Instructions for Nurses and Assistants.* **Rochester, MN: Saint Marys Hospital, 1920.**
Subsequent editions of the operating room text: 1924, 1928, 1937, 1952, and 1957.

Page 88   Interview with Sister Loretta Klinkhammer, January 28, 2000, and March 1, 2000.

Page 89   *A Century of Caring 1889-1989,* **p 36.**
Conversation between Sister Joseph and Dr. William J. Mayo.

Pages 89-90   **Clapesattle H:** *The Doctors Mayo,* **pp 595-598.**
Mayo Clinic's astonishing growth.

Page 90   **Saint Marys Hospital Annals, 1919.**
Contains financial data on the surgical pavilion.

Pages 90-91   **Saint Marys Hospital Annals, 1922.**
Describes the day of dedication.

Pages 91-92   *A Souvenir of Saint Mary's Hospital: Founded in Eighteen Hundred and Eighty-Nine,* **pp 60-67.**
Provides a detailed account of the pavilion.

Page 91   *Rochester Daily Post and Record,* **May 13, 1922.**

CHAPTER 6

Meeting the Challenges

hat was in the mind of the small woman who emerged from a corner of the room to stand before an applauding crowd? She was 66 years old, 44 years a Franciscan, 33 years at Saint Marys Hospital. Indeed, she may have been wondering, as one of the speakers suggested, how to find staff for the new challenges ahead. Likely, her thoughts were more personal and contained a prayer: "Dear God, thank you for blessing the work of our hands."

The surgical pavilion, which received such high praise that evening, stood in testimony to the achievements of Saint Marys Hospital. Yet Dr. William J. Mayo spoke with the conviction of personal experience when he said that bricks and mortar at Saint Marys were always secondary to the soul and spirit of the hospital. This chapter tells the Sisters' Story from within the walls during their prodigious building period. It focuses on persons who helped create the hospital's soul and spirit; one of those persons, Sister Joseph Dempsey, received this tribute from a major Catholic periodical: "... a woman whose name never appeared in the headlines, who wrote no books, and who was unknown to the world at large. Time and again colleges and universities had named her as the recipient of honorary degrees but, perhaps because she was too busy to leave her work, perhaps because she shunned whatever might seem publicity, she invariably declined, wording her refusal in terms which illustrated the courtesy and gentleness of her soul."

Uncomfortable with accolades, Sister Joseph typically deflected them by praising others. If asked about her deep religious faith and uncommon kindness, she quickly credited her parents and their example. When complimented for achievements, she pointed out the unstinting service of all

Sister Joseph Dempsey in 1922.
(From Saint Marys Hospital Archives.)

the Sisters at Saint Marys Hospital. Such self-effacing responses to individual praise, although genuine, should not obscure her deeply personal investment in the success and recognition of Saint Marys Hospital. Sister Joseph was a first-generation Irish-American, a woman of fierce loyalties to her faith, her family, and her institution—in that order. As an institutional leader, she preferred to use a velvet glove. When conciliation failed, however, Sister Joseph could be as scrappy and bare-knuckled as some of her forebears. She combined human compassion with tough-minded savvy and inspired these qualities among her Sisters. These qualities, intrinsic to the soul and spirit of Saint Marys Hospital, lived on as legacies long after Sister Joseph's time.

Sister Joseph had particularly high regard for Mother Alfred Moes. As a young Sister, she admired her superior's strong sense of direction and congregational achievements. In time, she recognized that Mother Alfred's vision succeeded at least in part because she commanded unquestioned authority. Sister Joseph was Mother Alfred's choice to head the hospital, but she went to her new assignment solely out of obedience. Leaving her work in education was a wrenching separation; as for nursing, initially she found it distasteful and humiliating. Religious conviction prompted her to take up the task with resolve and frontier resourcefulness. Sister Joseph believed that she did God's will by following the directive of her superior. She would do her best, give without counting the cost, and leave the outcome to God. This diminutive woman would have no difficulty claiming her authority. When questioned, she took a step back, fixed her challenger in the gaze of bright brown eyes, and asked, "Who's running this institution?"

On the frontier of Minnesota, the Sisters of Saint Marys Hospital continued a tradition of women called to a life of service which dated back to the early years of Christianity. Their belief in a personal calling empowered them with a sense of purpose and, with that, cultural as well as spiritual confidence and authority. Historian Barbra Wall noted a paradox between Sisters and other women leaders of the time: "Historical evidence challenges paradigms that equate service and caretaking primarily with weakness or subordination. Nuns' ethos of service, in fact, made them neither weak nor subordinate. The church conferred on them a certain dignity and prestige. Herein lies a paradox. Secular nursing leaders, who shared the zeal for progress, expertise, and optimism . . . typically saw obedience and service as retreats from power. Ironically, these very characteristics were routes to prestige and autonomy for nuns. Sisters' obedience earned them, within their Church, a position of status and respect, which they employed in their management of large institutions."

Faith in a personal call gave the Sisters of Saint Marys Hospital an overall sense of purpose and the confidence to achieve it. The practice of prayer sustained them day by day. Prescribed common prayer throughout the day brought balance to the intensity of caring for acutely ill patients. They particularly welcomed time for personal prayer at the beginning and end of each day. Sisters not on duty kept strict silence from night prayer in the evening until the conclusion of morning prayer the next day. The practice of Sacred Silence, a tradition that began with monasticism in the 6th century, provided a context for personal prayer. Many went to chapel early in the morning before common prayer to make the Stations of the Cross, a practice that originated with Saint Francis. Fourteen stations, placed along the chapel walls, depicted the crucifixion and death of Jesus. Sisters walked slowly around the dimly lit chapel and paused at each station to recall the event and pray. Their prayer was undoubtedly one of personal devotion, but also on behalf of patients, those with whom they worked, and needs beyond the hospital. In the evenings, weary from their labors, they often stayed in chapel after night prayer, grateful just to rest in the presence of God.

Sister Joseph was fervently devoted to religious practice; indeed, some people called the chapel her office. Faith in the providence of God and the practice of prayer were qualities that defined her. "The Lord will take care of it," was her response when she had accomplished all that she could. Rising at 4:00 a.m., she was in chapel for a holy hour before most others arrived. Like her parents, Sister Joseph had great respect for the priesthood and could never do enough for priests who came to the hospital. Sisters watched her from their places in chapel, amazed and sometimes amused, as she single-handedly served priests who offered Mass at the chapel altars. Going from altar to altar, she lit candles and rang bells for all she was worth. Afterward, she made sure they had a good breakfast; small wonder that the clergy held Sister Joseph and Saint Marys Hospital in such high esteem.

Franciscan hospitality was the rule at Saint Marys Hospital, regardless of religion, race, or poverty or wealth. The hospital was the Sisters' home, and they welcomed each person with friendliness and compassion. Their first objective was to make patients comfortable and, as much as possible, feel at home. On the nursing floors, Sisters paid special attention to individual patient needs. They went to considerable lengths to meet these needs, such as personally preparing a meal served on attractive china to tempt a failing appetite.

Over the years, patients and visitors commented on "the feeling of family" they found at the hospital. Foremost in creating this feeling were the Doctors Mayo, whose biographer describes them as "courtesy itself to their guests." On hospital rounds each day, Doctors William J. (Will) and Charles H. (Charlie) Mayo personally acknowledged patients, family members, and working staff with a word or smile. These highly accomplished, respected men set a remarkable example and raised the level of goodwill. For vulnerable patients, far from home and beset with illness,

Sister Fabian Halloran. (From Saint Marys Hospital Archives.)

it would be difficult to measure the full worth of such treatment. Sister Paula Leopold, who served as a surgical nurse, recalled that it was standard practice for Sisters, after a full day in the operating rooms, to call on recovering patients in their hospital rooms.

Sister Fabian Halloran, "the guiding light of patient care," was one of the founding Sisters whom Mother Alfred assigned to Saint Marys Hospital. A small, gentle woman, she weighed no more than a hundred pounds, but she moved patients in and out of bed as if they were the size of children. Like the other pioneer Sisters, Sister Fabian had no formal nursing training. In her first assignment as night nurse, Dr. Will showed her how to care for each patient. One patient was a woman who had received hypodermic injections for some time; he assured Sister Fabian that the patient would teach her how to give an injection, and the patient did. Hypodermic syringes and thermometers were medicine's most sophisticated equipment at the time; there were no laboratories for testing blood and no x-ray images. Physicians and nurses were almost entirely dependent on their abilities of observation. The skilled nurse learned, through years of experience, to distinguish between the pallor characteristic of anemia and the wan complexion of patients who were bleeding internally. Sister Fabian's diagnostic competence was legendary. Long before educators taught the psychological benefits of comforting patients, Sister Fabian greeted each of her patients with a kind word, then grasped one of their arms with her thin hand. By touching the patient's skin, she not only demonstrated her personal concern but also could tell whether they were feverish or chilled or had a rapid pulse.

Mayo Clinic physicians learned to put great stock in Sister Fabian's opinion. She was their last hope when things went wrong. In one case, E. Starr Judd, M.D., performed an emergency operation on an elderly man who subsequently had severe pneumonia. Despite constant care and treatment, the patient did not have improvement. "Will he live?" Dr. Judd asked Sister Fabian. "No, not unless we stop wearing him out," she replied. "Doctor, you know when a man is approaching 80, whether he has surgery or not, he must have rest and nourishment and he must be kept warm." He asked her to take over the entire care of the patient, and told his assistants, "Boys, Sister may cancel any and all orders that have been written, and you do whatever she asks." Immediately, she stopped traffic in and out of the room, closed the windows, gave the patient hot fluids, and asked the Sisters to pray. After 4 days the patient's condition improved, and a few weeks later he was dismissed.

Care for the poor was a priority for the Sisters, and they looked after patients who had material or spiritual poverty in various ways. Nurses on Sister Fabian's floor told how "she spent herself for poverty-stricken patients," such as washing and ironing gowns for those who had no friend or family member to care for these needs. Her special attention, however, went to persons whom she would never meet — American Indians living on reservations. Sisters recalled, "[she] was always picking up discarded clothing, washing, ironing, and mending it to send to the Indian Missions. She did that up to the end of her life."

Mayo Clinic physicians pledged to care for "anyone without regard to financial status, race, color, or creed." The Sisters liked to tell a story about Christopher Graham, M.D., their beloved house physician, which happened when physicians were scarce during World War I: The well-known Clinic rule, "First come, first served," was changed to "the needy first." Saint Marys' nurses long remembered how Dr. Graham, white-haired, weary, overworked, would say to someone clamoring insistently for his attention, "Here on my list are the names of two hundred people whom I must see first because they are poor and cannot stand the expense of waiting for medical help."

Christopher Graham, M.D.

Until 1906 the Sisters were the only nurses. A 180-bed hospital, Saint Marys was one of the largest and most advanced hospitals in the United States. Indeed, more operations were performed at Saint Marys Hospital than at any other U.S. hospital; in 1906, the total number was 4,770. Patients came from almost every North American and European country, as well as Asia, South America, and Australia. In the face of this remarkable growth, the Sisters realized that their small numbers involved in nursing, about 20 in all, would not meet future needs. Sister Joseph wanted to institute a training school for nurses to provide staff and give students the special advantages that Saint Marys Hospital could offer. The Doctors Mayo did not welcome the idea: "Dr. Charlie and I had always done our surgical work with the Sisters' help, and we were much concerned as to whether anyone could be taught, even by the Sisters themselves, to perform the duties of the nurse as well as they. We had absolute confidence, then as now, in this group of women who have no thought outside their duty to the sick."

The Mayos were also concerned about the potential quality of the school in view of rapidly growing nursing schools around the United States, which operated without established standards or even textbooks. In 1890, a year after Saint Marys Hospital opened, there were 35 training schools in the

United States, 10 years later there were 432, and by 1910 there were 1,096. The dramatic growth of hospitals accounted for the rapid increase in nursing schools, and many hospitals believed they could not survive without a training school to provide student labor.

Sister Joseph did not share the Mayos' doubts about nursing care from laypersons, but she agreed that the lack of teaching standards could pose serious problems. She believed that the quality of the school would depend on the kind of person selected to superintend it. Characteristically, she prayed, asked the Sisters to pray, and looked for a person who could provide proper leadership. One day, in the operating room gallery, the appearance and manner of a young woman visitor impressed her. The visitor, she learned, was Anna Jamme, a Catholic nurse just graduated from the new Johns Hopkins' Training School for Nurses. Sister Joseph talked with her as they toured the hospital, and her first impressions were confirmed by the young woman's intelligence. Before she left, Anna Jamme asked whether she might see the chapel and genuflected reverently at the entrance. "That was all Sister Joseph needed!" a friend recalled, "she had found the proper head for the nursing school." Miss Jamme was not long on the job before the Mayos and their associates agreed with Sister Joseph.

The school opened at the end of 1906 with a class of two, chosen from five applicants. Three others were admitted 4 months later, and 11 the following year, and applications were already coming in from states as distant as New York and Oregon. All of the nursing Sisters, including Sister Joseph, took the first full class under Miss Jamme's instruction. By 1914, the 2-year curriculum was expanded to 3 years. The training school at Saint Marys Hospital had advantages that could not be duplicated elsewhere. Student nurses, in the company of physicians, nurses, and scientists from all parts of the world, learned about every field of medicine from Mayo Clinic's highly trained specialists. In her 6 years as superintendent, Anna Jamme saw the school grow, prosper, and take its place as "one of the leaders among institutions of its kind." Mary Ledwidge succeeded Anna Jamme; under her leadership the State of Minnesota accredited the school in 1915.

Sister Joseph took great interest in the school and delighted in seeing and hearing about students, past and present. For their weddings, she made it a custom to give nurses substantial gifts such as pillows and blankets. She instituted an endowment fund to provide financial assistance for capable lay women who wished to enter the profession. The Saint Marys School of Nursing Alumni Association, organized in 1910, generously augmented

The classes of 1908, 1909, and 1910 of the Saint Marys School of Nursing march to the first commencement exercise. (From Saint Marys Hospital Archives.)

the fund, known now as the Sister Joseph Endowment Fund. Sister Joseph was also a strong advocate for the educational advancement of Sister-nurses. Sister Mary Brigh Cassidy, hospital administrator from 1949 to 1971 and herself a graduate of Saint Marys School of Nursing, praised Sister Joseph as the first hospital executive in the United States who made it possible for Sister-nurses to prepare themselves for hospital and nursing administration by attending major universities.

The outside world viewed the hospital as a great institution where miraculous medical feats occurred, but those who labored within the walls knew that miracles were primarily the result of hard work and long hours. Almost every Sister carried major responsibility either for a nursing floor or for an extensive service area. Regardless of the position, Sister Joseph made such assignments with little fanfare—often just a word from her in the dining room and a Sister was expected to take charge of an area almost immediately. In the summer of 1918, Sister Borromeo Lenz was 26 years old and a year out of nurses' training when Sister Joseph designated her superintendent of the new isolation hospital, assisted by Sister Dorothy Morgenthaler as matron. Earlier that year the Sisters had purchased the former Lincoln Hotel located a hundred feet east of the hospital and remodeled it for this use. Rochester hospitals needed a separate site to care for patients with contagious diseases. Sister Borromeo and Sister Dorothy prepared the 40-bed hospital for patients. No one, however, was prepared for the influenza epidemic that came suddenly in the fall.

The classes of 1928, 1929, and 1930 of the Saint Marys School of Nursing. (From Saint Marys Hospital Archives.)

The disease, which spread rapidly throughout the United States, broke out in a mild form in Rochester, then virulently in the hospital itself. On October 7, 1918, 20 persons, 18 of them nurses, had to be moved to the isolation hospital. The next day patients began arriving from all over the community. By the end of the week, the isolation hospital was overflowing, even to cots in the hallways. When patients died, more waited to be admitted. Sufficient nursing help was not available. Indeed, Saint Marys Hospital was so short of nurses and general help that staff worked night and day to the limit of endurance. They served wherever the need was greatest. With nurses from the floors, Miss Ledwidge, superintendent of nurses, worked in the laundry where help was completely depleted. Sisters Borromeo and Dorothy stoked the furnace, set up cots, cooked, and nursed patients and had only a few hours of sleep each night. Patients they thought would recover died the next day and patients whose conditions were thought to be hopeless went home completely well. By May, when the Rochester epidemic finally ran its course, 360 patients had been hospitalized for influenza and 41 had died.

The purchase of the hotel that became the isolation hospital was one in a series of major acquisitions around the time of the hospital's 25th anniversary in 1914. The Sisters made several land purchases to protect the hospital's boundaries and serve as future building sites. One of the prime properties the hospital gained during this time was a gift from Dr. Christopher Graham in honor of Mother Matilda Wagner on her 50th anniversary as a Franciscan in 1919. That same year the Sisters purchased a 200-acre farm, later named Saint Mary's Farm, and hired a full-time manager. A week after buying the farm, the Sisters signed contracts for $2,200,000 and began construction of the new surgical pavilion.

During the same period, the Mayos took several bold initiatives that had far-reaching consequences for their medical group. After decades of renting office space, they built a separate building on the site of the former home of Dr. William Worrall Mayo. Henry S. Plummer, M.D., designed and supervised construction of the 1914 Building. In addition, he formulated an organizational plan to integrate all the activities of the medical practice, which included research and education. The Mayos long believed that the advantages of medical specialization could be achieved only if specialists functioned as a unit in relation to the patient. "A sick man is

First Mayo Clinic building, 1914.

not like a wagon to be taken apart and repaired in pieces; he must be examined and treated as a whole." With Dr. Plummer's reorganization and a new separate building, Mayo Clinic emerged as a distinct institution, a complete clinic including laboratories housed under one roof. It was the world's first private integrated group practice of medicine, a new medical model.

Five years later, in 1919, the Mayo brothers extended their extraordinary generosity to future generations. They credited their father, William W. Mayo, for inspiring these remarkable achievements, indicating that their father recognized certain definite social obligations.

Henry S. Plummer, M.D.

He believed that a man who had better opportunity than others, and great strength of mind, body, or character, owed something to those who had not been so provided; that is, the important thing in life is not to accomplish for one's self alone, but for each to carry his share of collective responsibility.

The Mayo brothers established Mayo Foundation for Medical Education and Research, the first graduate program in the United States to train medical specialists, and endowed it with $1.5 million of their own savings. Next, they gave all of the physical properties and assets of Mayo Clinic to Mayo Properties Association, today known as Mayo Foundation: ". . . the Mayos, their partners and all future Mayo physicians would receive a salary and not profit personally from the proceeds of the practice. All proceeds beyond operating expenses were henceforth contributed to education, research and patient care."

Mayo Clinic and Saint Marys Hospital began a new stage of development. This watershed period for Mayo Clinic brought major changes for Saint Marys Hospital. The Sisters faced a new reality when the Clinic became a separate institution. Mutual trust, forged in their first 25 years, however, bonded them personally and institutionally. Determined to continue the partnership, Franciscans spared no effort or financial investment to attain that end. Hospital acquisitions anticipated the Clinic's initiatives and positioned them favorably to meet its future needs.

Preserving the institution of Saint Marys Hospital posed several challenges for Sister Joseph. The hospital's method of patient care, except for private duty nurses, involved one Sister assigned to each general floor, and the remainder of the staff were student nurses. Franciscans also were responsible for major service areas, such as the dietary, housekeeping, laundry, and business units. As the annual patient census climbed, they hired larger numbers of lay employees. Personnel figures from the 1928 annals of the hospital tell an important story:

Sisters	68
Student nurses	288
Graduate nurses	152
Maids	92
Men	43
Total	643

The categories of "maids" and "men" require some explanation. Women who worked as maids served in various service departments: the laundry, dietary department, and housekeeping. Men employees also had various positions: clerical worker, janitor, and farmhand. The hospital's radiology and pathology services were provided by Mayo Clinic, which paid Saint Marys for space, equipment, and other expenses.

Fortunately, Rochester and the surrounding area were extraordinary resources for skilled and dedicated workers. These women and men who shared the same rural values as most of the Sisters were hard-working, resourceful, generous, and loyal. Like the Franciscans, many of them came to Saint Marys Hospital and stayed a lifetime. The contribution of lay employees to the hospital cannot be overstated. Indeed, several volumes would only begin to chronicle stories of their service to patients with the Sisters of Saint Francis.

New employees received job training from the Sister in charge of their area. In addition to the specifics of their assignment, they learned about the hospital's mission and purpose, most often translated as "the patient comes first." Another high priority, also forcefully communicated by the Franciscans, was careful stewardship of hospital property. This value transcended job position and applied to everyone in every part of the institution. Meticulous in the care of material goods, Sisters practiced what they preached. They seldom threw a piece of paper away until it was used on both sides, and they mended sheets and linens so carefully that their use extended far beyond that of most institutions. Franciscans expected "a good day's work for a good day's pay and made no bones about it." Over the years employees liked to tell stories, mostly good-natured, about the Sisters. One of them was about Sister Dionysia Mentel, famous for enforcing frugality and hard work. "If you're looking for Sister Dionysia," one wag attested, "just sit down, and she'll be right along."

Sister Joseph had enormous appreciation for the employees of Saint Marys Hospital. She hired most of them herself and took an interest in each one; employees liked to call her "Mother Joseph." A solid bond of shared dedication among the Franciscans and their lay colleagues made them in many respects like one family. When death, illness, or unexpected tragedy struck employees or their families, Sisters immediately gave material and spiritual support. In turn, when the hospital was in dire straits, as with the influenza epidemic, Franciscans could count on employees' unstinting assistance.

As absolutely vital as employees were in the life of Saint Marys Hospital, Franciscans provided the institution's foundation. Clothed in white habits and present in every part of the hospital, they were powerful symbols for patients and staff. Beyond the symbol, however, Sisters were pragmatic, hard-working women. The son of a renowned Mayo Clinic neurosurgeon and a surgeon himself, Martin A. Adson, M.D., recalled that the Sisters made the system work for physicians and patients alike: "The system worked well because those Sisters commanded respect and not a little awe. They were removed from the rest of the world, dedicated, starched, and standing tall with a very impressive demeanor. The Sisters were bright and functioned well; they kept it all together. Their steadying aura of dedication allowed me and others to perform well. No question that the Sisters felt the patient came first, as did the physicians; this shared priority linked us and transcended lifestyles."

"Sister Gertrude [Gaertner] stepped out of the mold somewhat, but she could afford to because she was such an excellent practitioner. The rumor was that she could identify the kind of tumor just by palpating it. She wore a very loose habit, kind of like a jogging suit, and was known to say, 'We could use a little less prayer and a little more work.'"

The cultural backdrop of the frontier was fortuitous for Franciscans. Relatively unencumbered by outside influences, they could move forward with minimal interference. In the first part of the 20th century, religious congregations in the East that operated hospitals received unctuous letters emanating from the Vatican. The letters expressed concern about Sisters performing activities "not altogether becoming to virgins dedicated to God." They were particularly interested in whether men were patients, and asked whether Sisters bandaged, gave baths, or assisted in operations "on the bodies of men." No record of such a letter is extant in the Rochester Franciscan archives. Perhaps it was an oversight; more likely, the bishop of Winona, who had unquestioned trust in the Franciscans and the Doctors Mayo, simply took care of such questions.

Although outside forces did not significantly threaten the institution, differences within the congregation over the allocation of personnel and finances posed serious problems, particularly for Sister Joseph as administrator. Care for the sick and teaching were the order's primary works, but the numbers of Sisters in teaching far exceeded those at the hospital. In 1928, when the congregation approached 500 members, 68 Sisters served at the hospital; in 1939, of 600 Sisters, 77 served at Saint Marys. The majority of Sisters taught in diocesan schools, where reimbursement was not much more than convent housing and a small allowance for food.

The hospital had regular sources of revenue from patients. In addition, it attracted major donors. In 1922, for example, Charlotte Hill Slade, daughter of noted railroad empire builder J. J. Hill, gave the Sisters of Saint Marys Hospital $60,000 for a convent in memory of her mother, Mary Theresa Hill. As noted earlier, the Sisters at Saint Marys were careful stewards. Meticulous in the care of material goods, they also were astute businesswomen. They invested their earnings in hospital improvements and building projects; also, they regularly made a significant financial contribution to the congregation. Indeed, although the Sisters at Saint Marys made up less than 15% of the total congregation, hospital earnings contributed 80% of the order's financial resources.

With the appointment of Mother Leo Tracy as major superior, the congregation required increased amounts of revenues from the hospital. Mother Leo wanted monies for educational efforts, notably congregational schools and the College of Saint Teresa (a women's college established by the Franciscan Sisters in 1907). Sister Joseph, however, needed hospital revenues for substantial building commitments and renovations at Saint Marys Hospital. Mother Leo's 18 years in office, from 1915 to 1933, could be characterized as a period of conflict between her and Sister Joseph over distribution of the earnings from Saint Marys Hospital. Close in age, the two women came from

Mother Leo Tracy, General Superior from 1915 to 1933. (From the Assisi Heights Archives, Rochester, MN.)

similar backgrounds. Like Sister Joseph, Mother Leo was first-generation Irish-American whose parents fled the famine and settled on a farm east of Rochester. Both also had been public school teachers before entering the congregation. Their conflict deepened divisions within the congregation, presaged in events 40 years earlier when, after Mother Alfred proposed a hospital, Sister-teachers secretly reported against her to Archbishop John Ireland.

Bishop Patrick Heffron's irregular appointment of Mother Leo to major superior was an unfortunate beginning to her term in office. Bishop Heffron had succeeded the more conciliatory Bishop Joseph Cotter. Although supportive of Saint Marys Hospital, Bishop Heffron directed much of his prodigious drive to diocesan schools and colleges. He was highly invested in the College of Saint Teresa. Diocesan historian William Crozier made the point that the bishop promoted the college primarily to provide qualified teachers for parochial schools. Further, he wanted a Franciscan general superior who would concur with these goals: "To achieve his objectives Heffron intervened in the internal affairs of the Rochester Franciscans, actions bitterly resented by the congregation."

When Bishop Heffron presided over the 1915 election for major superior, the Sisters elected Mother Matilda Wagner on the first ballot. The bishop refused to accept the vote; he claimed that Mother Matilda's election required a two-thirds vote because she had been in office 20 years and the Church discouraged perpetuity. When the next three ballots failed to produce a majority, he closed the voting and left the room. On his return, he presented a written document appointing Sister Leo Tracy as superior general of the congregation. Sister Leo was a recognized leader and staunch advocate of the college and diocesan schools. The bishop allowed Mother Matilda's election as first councilor, but arbitrarily made his own appointments for the other councilors, among them Sister Joseph.

Congregational historian Sister Caedmon Homan described how the situation for Sister Joseph and Saint Marys Hospital changed with the appointment of Mother Leo: "When Mother Matilda administered the affairs of the Congregation as General Superior, Sister Joseph was more or less independent as to its personnel and finances. After Mother Leo was appointed by Bishop Heffron in 1915, however, decisive judgments concerning the administration of the hospital were made by him. Because Mother Leo did not always see the needs of Saint Marys Hospital as Sister Joseph thought she should, the latter often considered herself justified in having recourse to the bishop, just as Mother Leo herself did when she thought it imperative in order to secure the fulfillment of what, according to her perspective, was for the good of the congregation. In other words, Bishop Heffron acted as mediator between the two Franciscan leaders of great ability, but with divergent judgments and interests, both objectively praiseworthy."

During her 18 years of leadership, Mother Leo did not assign Sisters to Saint Marys Hospital. Instead, she required that they volunteer for the hospital and she considered their request. After the Saint Marys School of Nursing opened in 1906, a significant number of students chose to become Franciscans; some entered the order before finishing training. They hoped to return to the hospital, complete their studies, and stay on as nurses. Mother Leo, however, did not always concur with their hopes. In the middle of their nurses' training in 1930, three students joined the Franciscan congregation, Sisters Pauline Brick, Ermine Prew, and Janice Blee. After completing the novitiate, Sister Pauline asked Mother Leo whether she could go back to Saint Marys. The mother general, who could be abrasive, thundered a

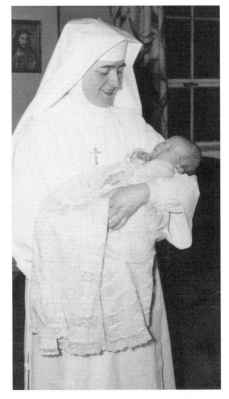

Sister Pauline Brick, who became supervisor of pediatrics at Saint Marys Hospital. (From the Assisi Heights Archives, Rochester, MN.)

reply to the young Sister. "Nurses! Nurses! We don't need nurses, we need teachers," and promptly sent her out to teach first grade. Later, Sister Pauline was allowed to return to the hospital and begin her notable years of service in nursing. Sister Janice, also sent out to teach, continued in education and excelled in the profession. Sister Ermine went back to Saint Marys immediately after the novitiate and served as an orthopedic surgical nurse until she retired 40 years later.

The disparity in numbers of Sisters at Saint Marys was a mixed blessing, and Sister Joseph used it to the hospital's advantage. Volunteers from congregational ranks were self-selected, highly motivated women. With some discretion, Sister Joseph must have looked for Sisters most likely to commit for an extended time. Self-selection, high motivation, and lifelong dedication created a cohesive Franciscan presence and ensured a high degree of esprit de corps. Moreover, years of experience had taught Sister Joseph how to manage with limited numbers of Franciscans assisted by an excellent staff of lay personnel.

Under Mother Leo, the order grew not only in numbers but also in congregational works, which included 35 schools in Minnesota, Ohio, Colorado, and Nebraska. Health care outside Rochester also flourished with the founding of Mercy Hospital in Portsmouth, Ohio, and several nursing homes. Cultural refinement and a lifelong love of learning were Mother Leo's goals for Sister-teachers. Typically, after completing their teaching assignments, Sisters went to the College of Saint Teresa. In summer school they took classes from Sisters on the college faculty toward completion of their academic degrees. Mother Leo carefully selected Sisters for the college faculty and sent them to major universities for preparation. Despite her enormous drive and vision, however, she lacked financial resources to achieve her ambitious plans.

Alternatively, at Saint Marys Hospital Sister Joseph looked after large amounts of earned revenue, but she was subject to strict congregational approval for spending them. In addition, such requests could be heard only at the congregational executive meetings, scheduled at the major superior's discretion. Such restrictions on capital were of particular concern. Sister Joseph needed timely access to resources in order to respond to hospital and Mayo Clinic needs. Already, she had experienced arbitrary resistance to her requests from contentious congregational administrators. Presumably, she was not inclined to continue spending excessive time and energies wrangling over monies.

Ultimately, Mother Leo and Sister Joseph struck a modus operandi, a practical arrangement to facilitate their separate institutional goals. Most likely, these two fierce Irish leaders understood the depth of the other's intractable resolve and came to terms. Rancorous congregational division was a bleak alternative that would not have suited either of them. Indeed, their personal disagreement from all accounts was unknown to most of the Sisters. Most likely, understandings reached by Mother Leo and Sister Joseph contributed to hospital acquisitions going forward with minimal congregational opposition. Mother Leo, in turn, invested significant monies in an extensive building project for the College of Saint Teresa. Unfortunately, large debts from these investments came due in the Great Depression of the 1930s. Struggling to keep financially afloat, the congregation looked to the revenues of Saint Marys Hospital as its lifeline.

Over the years, the hospital Sisters, largely because of their distinctive work, had become an almost independent community. Unlike the teaching Sisters, whose lives were determined by the school schedule and vacations, the hospital Sisters had little relief from their commitment to caring for the sick. Within the larger congregation, Sisters recognized the hospital's outstanding service and admired the Sisters' remarkable achievements. Hospital Sisters seldom saw other members of the congregation, and the two groups had little opportunity to know each other. One occasion for such exchange could have been at the traditional congregational gathering and meal, which celebrated the end of the Sisters' annual retreat. Without fail, however, immediately after retreat, cars waited for the hospital Sisters. They went home to Saint Marys Hospital, where Sister Joseph welcomed them warmly and they had their own celebration.

The Sisters of Saint Marys Hospital often recalled how they found inspiration from the dedication they observed in each other. Mutual regard and example strengthened them in their resolve to serve patients and continue the tradition that characterized the soul and spirit of Saint Marys Hospital. This achievement, which required rigorous diligence and personal discipline, was all the more remarkable given their small numbers. The next chapter moves beyond congregational conflict and continues the Sisters' Story in a context of new challenges, opportunities, and emerging leaders.

ENDNOTES

Page 97   **A Great Woman (editorial).** *America* **April 15, 1939;61:10-11.**
                     Tribute to Sister Joseph Dempsey.

Pages 97-98   **Homan MC:** *Years of Vision, 1903-1928: A History of the Sisters of*
                     the Third Order Regular of Saint Francis of the Congregation of Our
                     Lady of Lourdes, Rochester, Minnesota. **Unpublished Masters Thesis,**
                     Catholic University of America, Washington, DC, 1956, pp 102, 115.
                     Some of Sister Joseph's characteristics noted.

Page 99   **Marshall ES, Wall BM: Religion, Gender, and Autonomy: A**
                     Comparison of Two Religious Women's Groups in Nursing and
                     Hospitals in the Late Nineteenth and Early Twentieth Centuries.
                     Advances in Nursing Science **1999;22:7,9.**
                     Sisters and hospital leadership. Celibacy mandated separate space
                     for nuns, and it was in this space that they created and ran their own
                     institutions.

Page 99   Interview with Jane Campion, October 22, 1998.
                     "Sisters had an esprit de corps and a high sense of professionalism.
                     The hospital taught them to go into a new assignment, learn it quick-
                     ly, and always remember the needs of the overall institution. They
                     were encourged not to be ostentatious, rather, to be self-effacing and
                     generous. Sisters tended to stay home and learn because in many ways
                     they had more opportunities to learn at Saint Marys than elsewhere."

Pages 99-100   Interview with Saint Marys' Sisters: January 29, 2000, (Sisters Alice
                     Marie Burns, Amadeus Klein, Angelo Grose, Antoine Murphy, Cashel
                     Weiler, Charlotte Dusbabek, Dora Medina, Ellen Klooster, Frances
                     McManimon, Generose Gervais, Germaine Hullerman, Gildas
                     Klinkhammer, Janet McNally, Lauren Weinandt, Lucas Chavez, Mariana
                     Boltz, Mary Lou Connelly, Moira Tighe, Noreen Burke, Rose Gillespie,
                     Valerie Olson, Vera Klinkhammer). Aspects of the Sisters' daily life.

Page 100   Interview with Sister Paula Leopold, October 30, 1998.

Pages 100-101   **Erne J:** *Notes on Nursing History at Saint Marys Hospital.* **Saint**
                     Marys Hospital Archives.
                     Sister Fabian Halloran.

Pages 100-101   **Erne J: A Portrait of Sister Fabian.** *Saint Marys Alumni Quarterly,*
                 Spring 1941, pp 19-22.

                 Saint Marys Hospital Annals, 1922.
                 Dr. E. Starr Judd paid this tribute to Sister Fabian at the 1922 surgical
                 pavilion dedication ceremonies: "Sister Fabian is a wizard among the
                 patients. If we are in trouble about the diagnosis, or rather prognosis
                 of a patient, we call on Sister Fabian and she will tell us if the patient
                 is going to get well or not."

Page 102   **Clapesattle H:** *The Doctors Mayo.* **Minneapolis: The University of
                 Minnesota Press, 1941.**
                 Story about Dr. Christopher Graham **(p 568)**. The Mayos' reservations
                 about a nursing school **(p 499)**.

Pages 102-103   **Christy TE: Nurses in American History: The Fateful Decade,
                 1890-1900.** *American Journal of Nursing* **1975;75:1163-1165.**
                 Information on the history of nursing.

Page 103   Interview with Sister Lauren Weinandt, October 12, 2000.

                 Saint Mary's Training School. In: *A Souvenir of Saint Mary's Hospital:
                 Founded in Eighteen Hundred and Eighty Nine.* **Rochester, MN: Saint
                 Marys Hospital, 1922, pp 29-31.**

                 A Century of Caring: 1889-1989. **Rochester, MN: Saint Marys Hospital,
                 1988, pp 75-86.**

                 Stories about Miss Anna Jamme.

Page 103   The name of Saint Marys School of Nursing evolved from its founding.
                 First called "Saint Mary's Training School for Nurses," it was next called
                 "Saint Mary's School of Nursing." It is currently referred to as "Saint
                 Marys School of Nursing."

Page 104   **Cassidy MB: In Memoriam.** *Saint Marys Alumni Quarterly,* **Spring
                 1939, pp 6-7.**

Pages 104-105   *The Influenza Epidemic.* **Saint Marys Hospital Annals, 1918.**

                 A Century of Caring: 1889-1989, **pp 37-38.**

                 Description of the Influenza Epidemic of 1918 in Rochester.

Pages 105-106   *Land Acquired for and by Saint Marys Hospital.* **Saint Marys Hospital Archives.**

Saint Marys Hospital Annals, 1911, 1914, 1918, 1919.

Acquisition of land by Saint Marys Hospital.

Pages 106-107   **Nelson CW:** *Mayo Roots: Profiling the Origins of Mayo Clinic.* **Rochester, MN: Mayo Historical Unit, Mayo Foundation, 1990, pp 170-175.**

Page 106   **Clapesattle H:** *The Doctors Mayo,* **p 530.**

Mayo WJ: The Necessity of Cooperation in the Practice of Medicine. Rush Medical College Commencement Address. In: *Collected Papers of St. Mary's Hospital Proceedings of the Staff Meetings of the Mayo Clinic.* **Philadelphia: W. B. Saunders Company, 1910, pp 557-566.**
"The first effort made to meet the situation was in the development of clinical specialties. Man was divided for treatment into parts, as a wagon is divided in the process of manufacture. Each part of man was assigned to those who could devote special attention to their particular portion, giving the benefit of superior skill in treatment. Unlike a wagon, man could not be treated in parts, but only as a whole, and the failure to coordinate the various specialties quickly reduced their number. It became necessary to develop medicine as a cooperative science; the clinician, the specialist, and the laboratory workers uniting for the good of the patient, each assisting in the elucidation of the problem at hand, and each dependent upon the other for support."

Page 107   **Clapesattle (p 179).**
Dr. William Worrall Mayo's remarks.

Page 107   *Teamwork at Mayo.* **Brochure. Rochester, MN: Mayo Press, 1996, pp 11-12.**

Clapesattle (pp 590-593).

Summary statements on the Mayo Foundation.

Page 108   **Saint Marys Hospital Annals, 1928.**

Pages 108-109   Interview with Saint Marys Hospital Sisters, January 29, 2000 (see endnote on p 115).
Background information on Sisters and lay employees.

Page 109   Interview with Dr. Martin A. Adson, October 29, 1998.

Pages 109-110   **Coburn CK, Smith M:** *Spirited Lives: How Nuns Shaped Catholic Culture and American Life, 1836-1920.* **Chapel Hill: The University of North Carolina Press, 1999, p 203.**
                Reference to Vatican's concerns.

Page 110   **Saint Marys Hospital Annals, p 178.**
                Charlotte Hill Slade to Sister Joseph, October 28, 1922: "Because of my respect and affection for you, and appreciation of your wonderful accomplishment in St. Mary's Hospital—it is my happiness to offer you sixty thousand dollars ($60,000) for the construction of a convent building dedicated to the Blessed Mother and in memory of my mother, Mary Theresa Hill. This building will be to house the Sisters at St. Mary's, so many of you have been personally kind to me over a period of sixteen years."

Page 110   **Homan MC:** *Years of Vision, 1903-1928: A History of the Sisters of the Third Order Regular of Saint Francis of the Congregation of Our Lady of Lourdes, Rochester, Minnesota,* **p 104.**
                Makes this point about the donation: "Later permission was given to use the gift in remodeling the 1912 wing of the hospital for a convent." Footnote reads: "This statement by Sister M. Domitilla, December 29, 1953, personal interview. Minimal remodeling was completed in 1941. Gradual changes were made through 1949. In 1952, the fifth story was removed and replaced with entirely new construction (letter from Sister Mary Brigh Cassidy, April 11, 1955).

Page 111   **Crozier W:** *Gathering a People: A History of the Diocese of Winona.* **Winona, MN: Diocese of Winona, 1989, pp 256-258.**

Pages 111-112   **Homan (pp 15-17).**
                Background of Bishop Patrick Heffron and congregational election.

Pages 112-113   Interview with Sister Pauline Brick, September 17, 1999.

Pages 113-114   **Homan MC:** *Years of Expansion, 1928-1970: A History of the Sisters of the Third Order Regular of Saint Francis of the Congregation of Our Lady of Lourdes, Rochester, Minnesota* **(unpublished). 1975, pp 1-3.**
                Mother Leo Tracy's accomplishments chronicled in congregational history.

CHAPTER 7

Reform and Expansion

*I*n 1914, the Silver Jubilee of Saint Marys Hospital marked the beginning of the first movement for hospital reform that would affect not only Saint Marys but also every hospital across the United States and Canada. Two professional organizations had their roots in the reform movement, the Catholic Hospital Association and the American College of Surgeons. Both Saint Marys Hospital and Mayo Clinic contributed substantially to these developing organizations. The Sisters of Saint Marys Hospital took a leadership role in the Catholic Hospital Association from its beginning and enjoyed a close association with the organization for 60 years. The Mayo brothers, charter members of the American College of Surgeons, also figured importantly in the Catholic Hospital Association. The example of successful collaboration between a Catholic hospital and nonsectarian physicians presumably helped forge an important working relationship between the two professional organizations. Ultimately, the movement for hospital reform would succeed largely because of the collaboration of the Catholic Hospital Association and the American College of Surgeons.

Scientific advances during the first decade of the 20th century, as the Mayo story attests, made a major contribution to surgery. Although these advances were positive in most respects, they created significant problems for the surgical profession. By 1910, according to Clapesattle, American surgery was in a state of chaos: "Knowledge and technique had advanced to the point of demanding special training or experience, but there were no requirements for a surgeon other than the M.D. degree." In 1913, renowned surgeon Franklin Martin, M.D., of Chicago, organized the American College of Surgeons "to maintain the highest ethical and professional standards."

Members of the College elected Dr. William J. Mayo president of the organization and named Dr. Charles H. Mayo to the first Board of Regents.

Leaders of the College soon recognized that many hospitals were "unfit to allow adequate performance of surgery." Indeed, at the end of a 2-year national study, they found that only 89 hospitals met even minimal standards; the results were so discouraging that they chose not to publish the report. Robert Myers, M.D., assistant director of the American College of Surgeons, described hospital conditions: "Buildings, equipment and patient accommodations were often antiquated, unclean and unsafe; diagnostic facilities were grossly inadequate and unused; medical records were poorly written, if at all; privileges were rarely controlled; critical evaluation of the professional work was practically unheard of; the majority of the medical profession was hostile toward any effort of reform; and hospital executives were not anxious to offend doctors who provided patients and revenue."

In the face of opposition from physicians and hospitals, the College of Surgeons embarked on a program of reform and asked a leading educator to assist them. As Chancellor of the State University of Iowa, John G. Bowman, Ph.D., was well known for achieving medical reform in his institution's school of medicine. Bowman came to the College with a strong interest in implementing hospital reform. With a grant from the Carnegie Foundation, Dr. Bowman and the College took the lead and initiated a program of minimal standards for hospitals.

The American College of Surgeons chose Catholic hospitals to begin the reform program for at least two reasons. First, half of U.S. hospitals were Catholic institutions. Second, experience told them that hospitals supported by civic communities strongly resisted admitting flaws in the institutions they had built. In contrast, they perceived Catholic institutions as more homogeneous, less tied to local community control, and potentially more open to reform; later, Dr. Martin reflected on their decision: ". . . the Catholic hospitals, many of them the oldest in the two countries, contained more than fifty per cent of all the beds on the continent. What would their attitude be toward a survey of their institutions by the American College of Surgeons? . . . We decided to approach first the authorities of this great outstanding group of hospitals. As we viewed it, hospital standardization, to succeed, must be looked upon as a spiritual as well as an educational movement."

Self-initiated reform was, in the opinion of the American College of Surgeons, vital to the movement's success. An important goal, therefore, was collaboration with superintendents of Catholic hospitals, largely religious Sisters. These religious leaders, however, lacked an important resource for accomplishing reform. Unlike their colleagues in other professions, they had no national organization to provide educational programs and a forum for exchanging ideas. Directors of the College believed that a national Catholic hospital organization would offer such a resource. Interestingly, while surgeons in Chicago shared their ideas for a national Catholic hospital association, 100 miles to the north, a Jesuit priest in Milwaukee contemplated the same idea.

Father Charles B. Moulinier, S.J., 56 years old, a university professor and educational administrator, had recently been appointed Regent of Marquette University's School of Medicine. He was highly regarded, with marked success as an academician. According to Catholic Hospital Association historian Robert Shanahan, Father Moulinier also possessed an "engaging personality. A handsome man, he is remembered by everyone as the epitome of charm and courtesy. It was this wonderful blend of charm and sincerity that enabled this priest to meet people easily and become friends quickly."

Father Moulinier would need all of these qualities and more to accomplish his goal of establishing a national Catholic hospital organization. In the course of preparing for his new assignment, Moulinier met Dr. Bowman and his colleagues at the American College of Surgeons. Their rationale for hospital reform and establishing standards of practice impressed him. They, in turn, were interested in his opinions on a Catholic hospital organization. He concurred with them on the need for such an organization, but his goals went beyond hospital reform. Father Moulinier wanted, above all, an association that would enable Catholic hospitals "to take their place with the best hospitals in the country." He recognized, however, that the proposed organization's first order of business was preparing Catholic hospitals for standardization.

In the summer of 1914, Father Moulinier went to St. Paul, Minnesota, to hold a

Father Charles B. Moulinier, S.J., founder of the Catholic Hospital Association. (From Shanahan RJ: History of the Catholic Hospital Association. St. Louis: The Catholic Hospital Association, 1965. Copyright ©1965 by The Catholic Health Association. Reproduced from Health Progress with permission.)

retreat for the Sisters of Saint Joseph. Several of the Sisters who had responsibility for the congregation's hospitals asked to meet with him about hospital
reform. When he outlined requirements for reform, they asked how such
a task could be accomplished. Father Moulinier immediately replied, "by
organizing a Catholic Hospital Association." With the Sisters' strong
encouragement, he returned to Milwaukee and conferred with Archbishop
Sebastian Messmer. The archbishop heartily endorsed the proposed
association and promoted it among religious Sisters associated with hospitals
as well as with priests and bishops. In less than a year, Father Moulinier
convened the first convention of the Catholic Hospital Association, on June
24, 1915. Two hundred delegates from 43 hospitals in 12 states attended
the first meeting in Milwaukee. Historian Shanahan notes that Sister Joseph
Dempsey served as the first chairperson of the organization: ". . . Sister
Joseph, O.S.F. of the Sisters of St. Francis of Rochester, Minnesota, was
appointed and acted as chairman for the business meeting. Sister Joseph is,
of course, the famous supervisor of surgery at Mayo Clinic, St. Mary's
Hospital, Rochester, Minnesota."

Later, at the election of permanent officers, Father Moulinier reluctantly
agreed to become president. In his view, "the Catholic Hospital Association
belonged primarily to the Sisters," and he preferred that one of them become
president. Shanahan gives the reasons for his opinion: "This insistence on
the Association remaining in control of the religious was not only due to
the fact that 95% of the hospitals were owned by the religious but also
because there was frequently the failure of the clergy to understand fully
the professional knowledge and responsibility involved in hospital care."

Father Moulinier was pleased to have Sister Joseph and other religious
Sisters join him on the slate of officers: ". . . first vice-president, Sister Joseph
[Dempsey], O.S.F., St. Mary's Hospital, Rochester, Minnesota; second vice-
president, Mother Mary Richard, F.S.P.A., St. Francis Hospital, La Crosse,
Wisconsin; secretary, Dr. Maud R. Williams, Milwaukee, Wisconsin; treasurer,
Sister Marie Immaculate Conception, S.N., Misericordia Hospital,
Milwaukee, Wisconsin."

True to its first order of business, the Catholic Hospital Association made
rapid strides to ensure that Catholic hospitals established uniform standards
and practices. Speaking to this subject, Dr. Charles H. Mayo addressed the
Sisters at their second annual convention in 1916. He told them that the
American College of Surgeons had, of necessity, taken up the work of standardizing hospitals and explained that "all institutions which desire to be

recognized must come within state requirements." Dr. Charlie went on to say, "The greatest help is expected from this association of Catholic hospitals."

The American College of Surgeons' program got under way in April 1918. That summer, during its convention, the Catholic Hospital Association officially resolved to support the program. "[Members] agreed that a resolution be sent to Dr. William J. Mayo, president of the American College of Surgeons, to read as follows: 'Be it resolved: that we, the Catholic Hospital Association of the United States and Canada, now assembled in Chicago in our third annual convention, approve the work being done by the American College of Surgeons for the standardization of hospitals, and assure the College of our fullest cooperation in its endeavor for the betterment of hospitals and the resultant increased welfare of mankind.'"

The resolution pledged almost 600 hospitals to standardization. Dr. Bowman, recognizing the broader implications of the Catholic Hospital Association's action, publicly thanked the membership: "The resolutions which you have just passed make this meeting one of the most historic occasions for the medical profession which has ever been held on this continent. It means that not only Catholic hospitals but all hospitals will take up the standards of service to which you have pledged yourselves. It means real standardization of hospitals and it means standardization of doctors."

As president of the American College of Surgeons, Dr. William J. Mayo expressed his warm appreciation in May 1920 in the first issue of the Catholic Hospital Association's new journal, *Hospital Progress*. A month later, Dr. Mayo was able to thank many of the Sisters in person. Saint Marys Hospital and Mayo Clinic invited Sister delegates en route to the convention of the Catholic Hospital Association in St. Paul to be their guests in Rochester. Three hundred Sisters responded to the invitation; they toured the hospital, observed surgical operations, and visited Mayo Clinic. The visit to Rochester was as memorable for the delegates as for their hosts, the Doctors Mayo and the Sisters of Saint Marys Hospital.

Delegates to the Catholic Hospital Association agreed on hospital reform for medical and surgical services, but nursing reform was a different matter. As the movement gained momentum, nurses across the country took positions for or against nursing reform. An elite circle of nursing leaders, largely from prominent universities, led the reform movement. Caught up in the spirit that animated American medicine, they looked to reform to raise the professional status of nursing. They focused on standardizing nursing schools and proposed a national grading system. Many nurses, both religious and secular, strongly dissented. The reformers' strong emphasis on professional values eroded nursing's traditional commitment to service. Nurses, in the opinion of the dissenters, were called to a life of service that transcended status and professional recognition.

In the midst of this contentious climate, Saint Marys School of Nursing was in a favorable position, thanks largely to Sister Joseph. She decided that Sisters rather than laywomen should direct the school and chose an outstanding woman for the position. To that end, in 1918 the congregation sent Sister Domitilla DuRocher and Sister Paul Conley to Columbia University, the first Sisters to enroll for advanced studies at the university's Teachers' College, Department of Nursing and Health. Sister Domitilla would study nursing education and Sister Paul, hospital administration. In 1939 Sister Domitilla became Sister Joseph's successor as administrator of the hospital. Previously, as this chapter recounts, she had made significant contributions in nursing education locally and on state and national levels.

Lillian DuRocher, later Sister Domitilla, was the second of 10 children born in 1889 to LaCombe and Josephine LaFontaine DuRocher in Monroe, Michigan. She came to the Rochester Franciscans in 1910 with a unique family heritage. Most Sisters were first-generation Americans, but her French ancestors came to North America in 1708. Biographer Sister Charlotte Dusbabek, O.S.F., notes that Lillian inherited a subtle sense of humor from her father, along with other valuable traits: "That stern and sturdy man had a cheerful philosophy of life which helped overcome the obstacles experienced by many of the pioneer farmers. From her mother she inherited a love for beauty and quiet and deep religious nature."

As a nurse for neighbors all around, Lillian's mother influenced her desire to become a nurse. Josephine DuRocher also inspired her daughter's devotion to Saint Francis of Assisi: "The family had a French edition of his life from which the mother used to read. Often she would stress Saint Francis'

Sister Charlotte Dusbabek, O.S.F., biographer of Sister Domitilla DuRocher.

generosity, his love for the poor, and how gracious he used to be to the poorest of the poor."

When Lillian began her senior year at Saint Mary's Academy in Michigan, she acted on a decision that demonstrated her confidence and clarity of purpose. One evening, through the stovepipe in her room, she overheard her father talking with a good friend, the county superintendent of schools. They were discussing the shortage of teachers for the rural schools: 20 schools were without teachers for the fall term. When the superintendent asked whether Lillian could take one of the positions, her father told him, "she must finish high school first." The next morning Lillian went to the superintendent, volunteered her services, and in the evening told her parents she had signed a contract to teach. Eventually, her parents relented, and she taught in rural schools for 3 years until joining the Rochester Franciscans in 1910.

As a novice, Sister Domitilla finished high school and began college studies; subsequently she taught in a parochial school for 3 years. In 1915 she asked to go into nursing and entered Saint Marys School of Nursing,

Franciscan postulants, 1910. Sister Domitilla DuRocher is in the first row, second from left. (From the Assisi Heights Archives, Rochester, MN.)

where she excelled. Sister Joseph recognized her abilities and, as noted, after nurses' training she went to Columbia University for advanced studies. Sister Domitilla graduated from Columbia in 1920 with the degree of bachelor of science and a diploma in teaching and supervision. Her natural ability as a teacher combined well with nursing, and she excelled in the theory and practice of nursing. The 2 years at Columbia, however, gave her far more than academic preparation and credentials. Sister Domitilla entered an academic setting charged with energy and purpose. Faculty members, among the leaders of the movement for nursing reform, influenced her personally and professionally. The university offered broad, expanding opportunities; a description at the time captures the experience: "Hardly less valuable is the effect of the university atmosphere and surroundings on the student 'morale.' Ambition reacts to the atmosphere of intellectual competition; the student nurse is stimulated to do her best and take her place with credit among her fellow students. . . . She feels, too, a new sense of dignity and of the importance of her work through her recognition as a member of an educational institution."

Sister Paul Conley (seated). (From Saint Marys Hospital Archives.)

To some, Sister Domitilla appeared reserved and aloof. At least initially, this was certainly true for Sister Paul, who studied with her at Columbia. Sister Paul, warm and sociable, recalled that Sister Domitilla seldom spoke on their long train ride to New York City. Thinking she might have offended her, Sister Paul asked if anything was wrong. Her companion turned to her and said, "If I have something to say to you, I'll say it." Later, associates said that Sister Domitilla was aware of her reserve and tried to overcome it. Indeed, she said of herself, "You know I never talk when I'm working . . . I never talk much when I'm *not* working!" She found it easy, however, to overcome her reserve when she taught or spoke in public. Speaking to a group responsible for revising the national nursing curriculum, she sensed their apprehension and reminded them about Skippy's prayer in the comic section of the morning paper: "Oh God, give me strength to brush my teeth every night. But if you can't give me strength to brush my teeth every night, please God, give me strength not to worry about it!"

When Sister Domitilla returned to Saint Marys School of Nursing, she lost little time implementing what she learned. She personally selected the best lecturers from among the Mayo Clinic staff and supplemented the lectures with class discussion to make the subject more meaningful. In addition, she introduced laboratory work in the basic sciences. As Educational Director, Sister Domitilla was particularly interested in faculty development. Her instructors remembered how she cautioned them about teaching too much: ". . . as most young teachers tend to teach more than the student can possibly retain." Instead, she told them to teach principles and extend the student's interest beyond the last examination. One instructor recalled a favorite message: "Students aren't sausages to be stuffed and squeezed occasionally. They should be taught so that they could be depended upon to continue their learning on their own."

When New York became the first state to appoint inspectors of schools of nursing, Sister Domitilla initiated regular inspections of Saint Marys School of Nursing by the New York State Board of Nurse Examiners. These inspections were highly reputed, and the receipt of their approval was prestigious recognition. The inspection, however, was an onerous task. A student who helped Sister Domitilla prepare for inspection asked why they went to "all this work." Many years later she remembered the answer she received: "The practice of medicine and surgery at the Mayo Clinic [is] regarded as the 'best in the land,' and [I want] nursing to have a similar status. . . . You may be a good nurse but you will be a better one if you come from a good school of nursing."

At Saint Marys Hospital, dietetic theory and practice were important parts of nurses' training. Consequently, the examining team carefully scrutinized the compliance of the school of nursing with standards and made this note in their 1923 inspection: "Good provision is made for this service. This is in addition to a very fine teaching laboratory and a diet kitchen for service." Examiners may have known that Saint Marys Hospital had a tradition of excellence in food service long before outside agencies created standards.

The tradition began with Sister Fidelis Cashion, one of the founding Sisters of the hospital. Sister Fidelis came to the hospital in 1889, at the special request of Saint Marys' first superior, "to take charge of the cuisine." Her arrival a few days after the hospital opened was long memorable for a dinner she served the staff physicians as a mark of courtesy and of the appreciation the Sisters had of their interest in the new hospital. Sister Fidelis' ability as a caterer made them receptive to the praise they often heard in ensuing years of the high quality of meals served at the hospital.

Dietetics took on an expanded role at Saint

Sister Fidelis Cashion, one of the founding Sisters of Saint Marys Hospital, who came "to take charge of the cuisine" in 1889. (From Saint Marys Hospital Archives.)

Before 1920, the dietetic tray service at Saint Marys Hospital included this kitchen area, where portions were measured and placed on carts for delivery. (From Saint Marys Hospital Archives.)

Marys Hospital with completion of the surgical pavilion in 1922. Sister Angelica Osdoba, a "quiet wisp of a thing" and a nurse by training, helped plan and direct the new dietetic facility. Located on the ground floor, it extended from wall to wall of the wing, "providing an abundance of light and complete aeration throughout the year." Serving the patients hot food was the focus of extensive study and innovation: "Each floor for patients has three serving rooms. . . . A separate food cart of steam table construction is provided for each serving room. . . . The food elevator conveys the cart to its assigned floor, whence it is taken directly to the serving room, and the food served piping hot by tray service to the patient."

Before 1922, Saint Marys Hospital was exclusively a surgical hospital because the surgical demand left no hospital rooms available for patients with exclusively medical problems. The surgical pavilion, which doubled the number of beds, offered the Sisters a welcome opportunity to expand the hospital's services. Within the year, renovations in the older part of the building provided facilities and patient beds for the departments of medicine, pediatrics, and obstetrics. Under the direction of Russell M. Wilder, M.D., a key person in developing nutrition services at Mayo Clinic and Saint Marys Hospital, the hospital opened a special diet kitchen on the ground floor of the new surgical pavilion. He was assisted by Miss Daisy Ellithorpe, Rochester's first dietitian, who graduated from Stout Institute, Menominee, Wisconsin. She came to Rochester to work at Mayo Clinic in the medical section of David Berkman, M.D. Dr. Berkman and Miss Ellithorpe established the "dietetics service" for patients, a forerunner of the diet kitchen.

One of the outstanding pioneer leaders in dietetics, Florence Hazel Smith, came to Rochester in 1923 and headed dietetic services at Saint Marys Hospital for 4 years. Widely known and respected for her professional accomplishments, Miss Smith set high standards in her new position. A prolific writer, during her years at Saint Marys Hospital she founded and served as first editor for the *Journal of the American Dietetics*

Russell M. Wilder, M.D.

Association. Saint Marys Hospital was fortunate to have the leadership of both Daisy Ellithorpe and Florence Smith in the beginning years of expanded dietetic services. Sisters Joseph and Domitilla, however, believed that a Sister with educational preparation should eventually head the department. Sister Victor Fromm, who later called herself "a renegade nurse," recalled how she had just graduated from Saint Marys School of Nursing "when Sister Domitilla persuaded me to go into dietetics." Sister Victor and Sister Ephrem Reycraft went to Columbia University in 1925 for advanced studies in dietetics and nursing education, respectively, and returned with their degrees 2 years later. When Florence Smith left Saint Marys Hospital for the University of Chicago, Sister Victor took her place in 1927.

The rapid growth of the medical department at Saint Marys Hospital paralleled the growth of dietetics. Sister Victor organized dietetic services as a hospital department in 1928 and described the work of the department as twofold: ". . . the administration of therapeutic diets and the education of student nurses and patients." Diet therapy became one of the major forms of medical treatment. In 1923 the department served approximately 17,000 special-diet meals, and by 1939 the number had increased to 65,500.

Sister Victor Fromm. (From the Assisi Heights Archives, Rochester, MN.)

Saint Marys medical department conducted extensive clinical investigations that required carefully controlled food intake for diseases such as diabetes mellitus, nephritis, osteoporosis, arthritis, and Addison disease. Commenting on the contribution of these studies, Dr. Wilder wrote, "It could be said that clinical investigation at Saint Marys stimulated the rapid development of dietetics."

Dietetic education took several forms, among them group lectures and demonstrations to patients and individual instruction. In 1923, an unusually large number of patients with diabetes were admitted to the medical department. With the discovery of insulin the previous year, patients came for instruction on its use. To facilitate learning about diabetes and other diseases, dietitians wrote booklets for distribution to patients and families. Over the 10-year period from 1923 to 1933, the medical staff of Mayo Clinic and dietitians at Saint Marys Hospital jointly developed and published most of the therapeutic diets. Miss Smith first gathered them in loose-leaf notebooks. Subsequently, Sister Victor compiled them into a diet manual; published in 1932, it was revised in 1935 and 1940.

Education of student nurses in the fundamentals of food selection was a high priority for the dietitians. Students received formal classroom lectures and extensive hands-on experience in the diet kitchen. Nationally recognized for their work with nurses, the dietitians collaborated with the American Dietetics Association and the League of Nursing Education, who published texts on the subject.

As the reputation of the department of dietetics grew, an increasing number of students, national and international, asked to study at Saint Marys Hospital. European fellows of the Rockefeller Foundation came from England, Poland, and Yugoslavia for postgraduate study in the department. In response to these numerous applications, Sister Victor organized an internship program in dietetics in 1930 with approval from the American Dietetics Association. Nine years later, the Fiftieth Anniversary Report of Saint Marys Hospital carried this description of the program: "The course, which originally was eight months in length but which was increased to twelve months in 1933, is designed to offer young women practical experience in preparation for the profession of dietetics. It is comparable to a medical internship and is to be considered a utility preparation for hospital and clinical dietetics. . . . The total number of dietetic interns trained up to the present time is seventy-three."

Responsibility for the hospital's main kitchens became a function of the dietetics department in 1938 under the supervision of Miss Lottie Crecelius. Officially called the Division of Food Production and Distribution, a hospital document described the wide scope of this assignment: "The activities of the Division of Food Production and Distribution fall into logical sequence. Menus are planned first, followed by requisitioning of food, assisting with food purchasing, assisting with the receiving and storage, preparing and cooking the food, and finally delivering it to the serving stations."

Fortunately, the Sisters had years of experience accomplishing such activities and the change was largely administrative. Sisters in housekeeping, laundry, and food service were essential to the hospital. Almost all came to their assignments as young women right out of the novitiate, and they stayed in domestic work for 40, 50, even 60 years. Although their work was behind the scenes, they were as committed to serving patients as any Sister in the surgery department or on a nursing floor. Further, they recognized the importance of their contribution and took great pride in the accomplishments of Saint Marys Hospital and Mayo Clinic. Many of them were of Polish descent and had strong faith, strong constitutions, and, some-times, strong opinions.

Sisters in food service worked in the main kitchens, in the gardens and henhouse behind the hospital, or at Saint Mary's Farm. Besides working in the garden and taking care of chickens, Sister Julia Wilhalm washed dishes in the Sisters' dining room. When, in her opinion, Sisters took too long talk-ing over a meal, she rang a bell, a signal for them to stop visiting and bring her their dishes. Those unfortunates who failed to drink all of their water got another scolding from Sister Julia. Interestingly, it was Sister Julia whom Sister Domitilla chose most often to accompany her to various meetings around the country.

Sister Julia Wilhalm. (From Saint Marys Hospital Archives.)

As a young pharmacist, Sister Quentin McShane remembered how the Sisters in the kitchen looked after her: "Sister Polycarp [Rozulanska] worried I wasn't getting enough to eat. When I told her my favorite was cream cheese and jelly sandwiches, she made them so often I asked her to stop—I was gaining too many pounds! I remember how Sister Polycarp and Sister Pacifica [Schubertowitz] made French toast and put on pancake parties just for the Sisters."

Sister Antoine Murphy, in charge of the orthopedics floor, had great affection for Sister Barnabas Schroeder, as did many others: "She was a saint, always a smile, always ready to help you. We had a very sick patient who was on a circular bed with extensive injuries. He wouldn't eat and I told the patient we would bring him anything he wanted. Fried mush and pork links were what he wanted and Sister Barnabas provided the makings for 'the best fried mush he'd ever tasted!'"

Saint Mary's Farm was a vital part of the hospital for more than 60 years. Raising their own livestock, fruit, and vegetables provided the Sisters with a regular source of fresh food of the highest quality to serve patients. During the first 30 years, Sisters and employees raised cattle and hogs and hundreds of chickens and grew grain to feed them on 10

Sister Barnabas Schroeder, preparing some of her famous donuts. (From Saint Marys Hospital Archives.)

acres behind the hospital. Employees milked the cows by hand to provide dairy products for the patients. The Sisters tended a large vegetable garden and carefully cleaned and prepared the fresh produce for the hospital kitchens. In 1919 Saint Marys Hospital purchased a 212-acre farm about 4 miles west of the hospital. For the next 3 decades the farm supplied the majority of milk for the hospital. The milk was pasteurized at the hospital, which used about 245,000 gallons annually. Sister Ludovica Rybinski was in charge of the pasteurization room and, with her helpers, bottled most of the milk. Sister Ludovica was also ambassador to the farm. Every afternoon Sister Julia and Sister Natalia Rybinski would accompany her to take food to the farmhands, look after the flock of turkeys and chickens, and "keep an eye on things."

Visiting the farm for a firsthand look at the sanitary production of the hospital's milk supply was a highlight for dietetic interns and nursing students. The farm was an important part of the Sisters' Story. From its

The Sisters raised chickens behind the hospital for many years. (From Saint Marys Hospital Archives.)

In 1919, Saint Marys Hospital purchased a 212-acre farm 4 miles west of the hospital. (From Saint Marys Hospital Archives.)

beginnings in the backyard of the hospital, the Sisters took an intense interest in the gardens, animals, and workings of the farm. For many, it recalled their rural childhood, and all took pride in the products that provided patients with tasty, nutritious meals.

As the next chapter attests, in the Great Depression of the 1930s Saint Marys Hospital suffered serious financial losses. The farm and hospital gardens were precious assets for the Sisters, who gave thanks to God for blessing the work of their hands with ample food and nourishment for their beloved patients.

ENDNOTES

Pages 119-120   **Clapesattle H:** *The Doctors Mayo.* **Minneapolis: The University of Minnesota Press, 1941, p 492.**
Status of surgery in 1910.

Pages 120-123   **Shanahan RJ:** *The History of the Catholic Hospital Association: 1915-1965; Fifty Years of Progress.* **St. Louis: The Catholic Hospital Association, 1965, p 19.**
Definitive history of the Catholic Hospital Association for this period. Shanahan notes: "In the year 1913, through the inspiration and leadership of Dr. Franklin H. Martin, one of the most renowned surgeons in America at that time, the American College of Surgeons came into being."

Page 120   **Shanahan (pp 25-26).**
Dr. Robert Myers' assessment of conditions existing in hospitals.

Page 120   **Shanahan (pp 27-28).**
Describes Dr. Bowman's background.

Page 120   Dr. Franklin Martin's comments from an unpublished paper, 1955. Cited by **Shanahan (p 26)**.

Page 121   **Shanahan (p 82).**
Describes Father Charles B. Moulinier.

Pages 121-122   **Shanahan (pp 6-9).**
Father Moulinier's contact with Sisters of St. Joseph in St. Paul and the beginnings of Catholic Hospital Association.

Page 122   **Shanahan (p 12).**
Note on Sister Joseph Dempsey serving as first chairperson.

Page 122   *Transactions of the Catholic Hospital Association,* **1915, p 170. Cited by Shanahan (p 14).**
Father Moulinier's reluctance to assume presidency of the Catholic Hospital Association.

Page 122   **Shanahan (p 47).**
Moulinier's rationale for Sisters assuming leadership of the Catholic Hospital Association.

Page 122   Shanahan RJ: *The History of the Catholic Hospital Association: 1915-1965; Fifty Years of Progress*, p 13.
                  Officers of the Catholic Hospital Association listed.

Pages 122-123   **Shanahan (p 29).**
                  Reference to Dr. Charles H. Mayo's speech to the 1916 convention of the Catholic Hospital Association.

Page 123   *Transactions of the Catholic Hospital Association*, 1918, p 14. **Cited by Shanahan (pp 32-33).**
                  Resolution by the Catholic Hospital Association to Dr. William J. Mayo and Dr. John G. Bowman's commentary.

Page 123   *Hospital Progress* **1:41-42, May 1920.**
                  Dr. William J. Mayo's letter to the Catholic Hospital Association members.

Pages 123-124   **Burgess MA:** *Nurses, Patients, and Pocketbooks.* **New York: Committee on the Grading of Nursing Schools, 1928.**

                  Donahue MP: *Nursing: The Finest Art; An Illustrated History.* **Second edition. St. Louis: Mosby, 1996.**

                  Kalisch PA, Kalisch BJ: *The Advance of American Nursing.* **Third edition. Philadelphia: JB Lippincott, 1995.**

                  Melosh B: *"The Physician's Hand": Work Culture and Conflict in American Nursing.* **Philadelphia: Temple University Press, 1982.**

                  References consulted on nursing and nursing reform.

Pages 124-127   **Dusbabek MH:** *The Contributions of Sister M. Domitilla Du Rocher, O.S.F. to Nursing, 1920-1939.* **Unpublished dissertation. Catholic University of America, Washington, DC, 1962, pp 8,9,12.**
                  This is an excellent resource on the life and contributions of Sister Domitilla. (When Sister Charlotte Dusbabek wrote the dissertation, she was known in religion as Sister Mary Henry. She later chose to return to her baptismal name, Sister Charlotte.)

                  Saint Marys Hospital Annals, 1920-1939.
                  Offers another resource on Sister Domitilla during her years at the hospital and contains extensive documentation of her leadership in

nursing education on the state and national level.

Page 126   **Committee for the Study of Nursing Education, 1923, p 483. Cited by Donahue MP:** *Nursing: The Finest Art; An Illustrated History,* **p 336.** Quotation on the influence of a university setting.

Page 126   **Dusbabek MH:** *The Contributions of Sister M. Domitilla Du Rocher, O.S.F. to Nursing, 1920-1939,* **p 12.** Sister Domitilla's personal reserve.

                The story about Sister Paul from an interview with Sister Charlotte Dusbabek, September 23, 1998.

Page 127   **Dusbabek (pp 25,27).** Sister Domitilla as educational director.

Pages 127-131   Several persons offered invaluable understanding on the early history of dietetics at Saint Marys Hospital in a succession of interviews during 1998-2001. They include Sister Moira Tighe, O.S.F., Karen Moxness, R.D., Stephen W. DeBoer, R.D., and Jean Mortenson, R.D. In addition, the writer is grateful to Mr. DeBoer for sharing many of his historical references on the history of dietetics. This material included a general history of the discipline and its practice in Rochester, Minnesota, from its inception as well as specific information about Saint Marys' Dietetics Department and Mayo Clinic's Nutrition Department. The writer is also grateful to Jean Mortenson, R.D., for her extensive and helpful papers on the history of Dietetics and to the Department of Dietetics, Saint Marys Hospital.

Pages 127-131   **Report of the Department of Nutrition. In:** *Saint Marys Hospital's Fiftieth Anniversary Report.* **Rochester, MN: Saint Marys Hospital, 1939.**

Pages 127-128   **Saint Marys Hospital Annals, 1923.** The survey report on the Saint Marys School of Nursing contained a section on dietetics.

Page 128   **Saint Marys Hospital Annals, 1933.** Sister Fidelis Cashion died October 20, 1933. A memorial recalls her important contributions.

Pages 128-129   *A Souvenir of Saint Mary's Hospital: Founded in Eighteen Hundred and Eighty Nine,* **1922, p 63.** Comments on supplying hot food to the patient's bedside.

Pages 129-131   **Saint Marys Hospital Archives.**
History of Mayo Clinic's Nutrition Department. Unpublished paper.
June 5, 1979.

Wilder, Russell M., B.S., Ph.D., M.D., F.A.C.P. In: *Physicians of the*
Mayo Clinic and the Mayo Foundation. **Minneapolis: The University**
of Minnesota Press, 1937, pp 1458-1463.

Interview with Karen Moxness, R.D., October 2, 1998, and October 25,
1999.

Page 129   **Florence Hazel Smith: 1887-1971.** *Journal of the American Dietetics*
Association **58:547, June 1971.**
Tribute.

Pages 129-131   **St. Marys Hospital Archives.**
Klause V: Clinic Nutrition Department. Unpublished paper. June 5,
1979, pp 1-5.

Pages 129-131   *Report of the Department of Nutrition: Saint Marys Hospital,*
Rochester, Minnesota, **1939. Unpublished paper, pp 1-6.**

Pages 130-131   Sister Victor Fromm's recollections are contained in numerous articles
at the time of her retirement.

Pages 130-131   **Saint Marys Hospital Annals, 1930-1939.**
Internship program in dietetics.

Pages 131-132   *The Annual Report of the Department of Nutrition.* **Saint Marys**
Hospital Annals, 1926, pp 66-67; 1930, pp 78-79.
The rapid growth of the dietetics department.

Page 131   **Victor M:** *Diet Manual: St. Mary's Hospital.* **First, Second, Third**
edition. Rochester, MN: St. Mary's Hospital, 1932, 1935, 1940.

Pages 131-135   Interview with Saint Marys Sisters regarding Saint Mary's Farm and
the Sisters in domestic service, January 20, 2000.

Page 132   Interview with Sister Quentin McShane, September 14, 1998.

Pages 132-133   Interview with Sister Antoine Murphy, September 21, 1998.

CHAPTER 8

Leaving the Legacy

The 1930s, years of the Great Depression, frame the last chapter of the Sisters' Story of Saint Marys Hospital. Worldwide financial decline began with the stock market crash of 1929. Within the year, 1,300 banks failed, followed by an extended period of business disasters and unemployment. Saint Marys Hospital had weathered the economic depressions of 1893, 1907, and 1921 with relatively few problems. Even in difficult times, most people found the wherewithal to take care of their health. The depression of the 1930s, however, was markedly different. Widespread, prolonged unemployment made people reluctant to come to Saint Marys Hospital for treatment, and those who came often had no money to pay their bills. In 1931, patients numbered 6,527, less than half the number recorded 3 years earlier. The next year, hospital registrations sank to 40% of capacity.

The dramatic decline in numbers of hospital patients resulted in limited employment for graduate nurses. The Saint Marys School of Nursing reduced the size of classes with the hope that smaller numbers of graduates would have a better chance to find work: "The Sisters did their best to find work for recent graduates and attempted to spread the work around so everyone could make at least a little money. Rose Pendle, the mother of two children, supplemented her husband's meager income of eighty dollars per month by occasionally working as a private-duty nurse for five dollars a day. The hospital tried to find ten days of work per month for its single nurses; then, after one year, encouraged them to go home to live with their parents."

Hungry people came to the hospital asking for food, and Sister Joseph Dempsey wanted no one turned away. Word of her kindness spread, and people regularly showed up at the kitchen, hoping to do some extra work in exchange for a meal. Sister Barnabas Schroeder usually asked them to mop the floor before feeding them; she remembered that the kitchen floor gleamed as never before in those lean years.

The depression had drastic consequences for the Franciscan congregation. Large debts for an extensive building project at the College of Saint Teresa came due in the early 1930s. Struggling to keep financially afloat, the congregation looked to Saint Marys Hospital for its lifeline. Earlier, Sister Joseph had established a fund for building a larger chapel; the chapel fund offered a source of immediate revenue. Between September 1932 and January 1933, the congregation borrowed more than $50,000 from the fund to cover financial obligations. Hospital monies would continue to play a vital role in meeting the congregational debt.

After 18 years as general superior, Mother Leo Tracy left office in July 1933. "With marked unanimity" the Sisters elected Mother Aquinas Norton, known for "organizational ability and financial genius." The new mother general was liable for a debt of $5 million owed to 5,000 note-holders. Mother Aquinas later confided that the day after her installation, the sheriff came to her office about overdue notes. The congregation's broker, hired to administer repayment of the notes, had misused the Sisters' money for his own purposes. The congregation lost $350,000; immediate action was imperative. The astute Mother Aquinas appointed Sister Adele O'Neil as congregational treasurer. Young, lively, and petite, Sister Adele possessed disarming financial expertise and dogged determination.

Francis M. Kelly, bishop of Winona, and his financial advisors met with the Sisters about the debt. To their surprise, the diminutive Sister Adele spoke up and suggested that she serve as broker rather than pay a large commission. Given the desperate situation, they agreed. Later, Sister Adele told the astonishing story of how she repaid the noteholders and "no one lost a dollar of principal." Sister Rita Rishavy from the hospital, highly able in business affairs, assisted her. Eighty percent of the creditors were people from Chicago, and Sister Adele sought assistance from a large Chicago bank. As she put it, "we made friends with the Continental Bank of Chicago and found the vice president very helpful." He gave her regular use of a conference room with telephone and typewriter. The room was adjacent to the office of the legal advisor, who offered his services as needed. Thus began the financial odyssey of Sister Adele and Sister Rita to and from Chicago, twice weekly, over the next several months.

The Chicago Northwestern Railroad, which served Rochester, gave free passes to religious Sisters. Because there was no day train, the Sisters took the night train to and from Chicago. On arrival in Chicago, they stopped at a downtown church for Mass, then went to the Continental Bank on Michigan Avenue. They worked the full day, calling creditors and asking them to renew their notes at a lower percentage. "Anyone of them could have thrown us into bankruptcy," Sister Adele reflected, "but they gladly agreed in order to save their principal." Returning to Rochester, they went directly to the motherhouse and wrote creditors, often until midnight, without benefit of any

Sister Adele O'Neil. (From the Assisi Heights Archives, Rochester, MN.)

office machines except a manual typewriter. After a day, sometimes two, they went back to Chicago and repeated the process. "Through it all," Sister Adele was quick to say, "We never missed our prayers." Six years later, when the hospital needed $8 million for a new medical building, the Continental Bank made the loan without a commitment fee. In addition, when Sister Adele went back to the noteholders for money, almost all were willing to reinvest. "From then on," she said, "we were our own brokers."

At the time that the congregation borrowed monies from the chapel fund, a new chapel was already under construction. By 1930, the fund was sufficient to begin work on a chapel. Sister Joseph made this note in the hospital Annals: "No hospital earnings were used for the chapel. Donations for the Chapel Fund were accumulated over a long period of years. Names and addresses of donors were not recorded, as whatever they gave was a voluntary offering for which they neither asked nor expected any reward, privilege, or even credit in this world. Many requested that no mention be made of their names. There were wealthy donors who out of their abundance gave large sums; there were others whose tiny gifts may have meant greater sacrifices. God will reward them all, but to these and all other benefactors, the Sisters owe grateful, prayerful, and lasting remembrance."

From its beginnings in 1889, Saint Marys Hospital had a small chapel, and 4 years later an enlarged chapel replaced the first one. In 1903, Victor Cordella designed a third chapel; Italian artists and artisans executed his design. The chapel's Italian influence was visible in the design of the arched ceiling and the beloved angel figures. Although perfect in detail, it was soon too small for the growing numbers of Sisters, hospital personnel, and students. On Sunday mornings it was not uncommon to find people kneeling far down the corridor, unable to enter the crowded chapel.

Saint Marys Chapel, 1903. (From Saint Marys Hospital Archives.)

Completed in 1932, the new chapel incorporated the lovely 1903 chapel within its structure. Located at the east end of the hospital, it seated 400 and contained an open concourse to accommodate wheelchairs. An article from *Saint Mary's News Bulletin* describes the chapel: "Basilica in style, Saint Marys Chapel is unique among hospital chapels. The simplicity of design, the high vaulted nave flanked by stately columns and softly illuminated by the mellow light diffused through the amber cathedral glass of the large

Saint Marys Chapel, 1932. (From Saint Marys Hospital Archives.)

arched windows, produce an effect of peace and quiet in striking contrast to the busy hospital world just outside the doors."

Materials used in the chapel came from all over the world: marble for the floors and walls from Germany, Spain, and Italy; pearl white granite for the columns from Minnesota, and oak for the pews and choir balcony from Appalachia.

Musicians commented on the quality of the chapel's Aeolian-Skinner pipe organ. The hospital annals tell the story of the pipe organ: "In the spring of 1932, among the patients on Sister Fabian's [Halloran] floor was a refined and scholarly man who told her to ask Sister Joseph to let him have something to say when we were ready to order the pipe organ. . . . He gave Sister Fabian some account of his musical credentials, to which she paid far less attention than she did to his critical condition, for he was very frail and very ill."

Sister Joseph welcomed the man's assistance. In due time, he prepared specifications for the organ, gratis, supervised the contract, and inspected it on his trips to Mayo Clinic. He told Sister that if she would let him know when the chapel was to be dedicated, no matter where he happened to be, he would come and play the organ for the services that day. . . . He was Emil Johan Oberhoffer, founder of the Minneapolis Symphony Orchestra and for 19 years its conductor.

Saint Marys Hospital was blessed from the beginning with excellent priest chaplains. For more than 50 years, the bishop assigned only one priest to the hospital. Father Francis Tracy, who served at Saint Marys Hospital from 1912 to 1918, was highly regarded as a chaplain and loved for his wit. In a talk to the Catholic Hospital Association, he recalled his brief instructions from Bishop Patrick Heffron when he became the hospital chaplain: "Don't interfere." Father Tracy went on to say that the chaplain should be on good terms with everyone in the hospital—if possible: "His relation with the interns ought to be of the most cordial character; they are ordinarily big, broad-minded, well informed, companionable. . . . At Saint Mary's, Rochester, we get along exceptionally well. The chaplain never yet essayed to instruct the interns as to how they should care for their patients, and up to the present no intern has manifested the slightest inclination to conduct the Sunday evening devotions."

Father Raymond Galligan came to Saint Marys Hospital in 1930 and served patients, staff, students, and Sisters until 1954. Father Galligan covered every floor of the hospital, calling on Catholic patients three times each day. Reliable as clockwork, the nurses remembered he almost sprinted as he arrived in the patient's room: "'My name is Galligan,' he would say. 'How are things going today?' A few kind words later, he would salute the patient again, and be gone. He did not have much time, but he had enough to convey to the patients that he cared, and more important, that God cared."

Father Galligan kept a horse in the barn behind the hospital and sometimes slipped out for a ride: "Nothing is so good for the inside of a man," he liked to say, "than the outside of a horse."

As in the past, a congenial exchange of ideas, if not always agreement, marked the relationship between the church hierarchy and Mayo Clinic physicians. The churchmen did not question the integrity of the physicians to abide by Catholic teachings at Saint Marys Hospital. Presumably, the Sisters' unqualified trust in their Mayo Clinic colleagues over many years influenced their opinion. The physicians invited Archbishop John Gregory Murray of St. Paul as a featured speaker when they hosted the Minnesota State Medical Association for the first time in 1933. Archbishop Murray, who spoke about the high ideals of a physician's calling, also warned against control of the medical profession by the state.

Archbishop Murray visited Saint Marys Hospital often; Sister Joseph was a favorite, and he frequently stopped by her office. On one occasion he met her sister, Sister Beatrice Dempsey, assigned to the hospital after retiring from teaching. The archbishop delighted in recounting Sister Beatrice's response to his question about her position: "Position? I have no official position. But I can tell you, archbishop, I'm much busier than all the rest of them put together!" According to Sister Regina Buskowiak, none of the Sisters had cause to apologize for their dedication to serving patients. Sister Regina was one of many young women who came to Saint Marys Hospital to

Father Raymond Galligan, Saint Marys Hospital chaplain from 1930 to 1954. (From Saint Marys Hospital Archives.)

study nursing and ultimately entered the congregation: "I was very impressed with the sisters particularly for their kindness and they seemed so dedicated. I wanted to become a sister, but wondered if I should wait until I finished training. I talked it over with Father Galligan, and he said, 'I think you should go now.'"

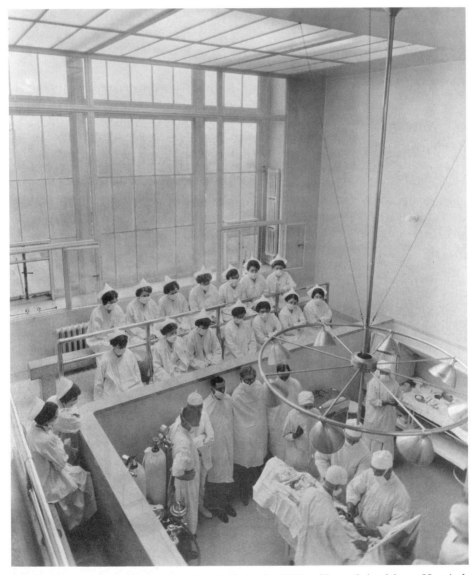

Student nurses observing an operation in the early 1920s. (From Saint Marys Hospital Archives.)

Sister Frances McManimon, a nursing student who became a Franciscan, had never known Sisters before and recalled how impressed she was with them professionally "and as warm human beings: They were models for me. Sister Monica [White] was a night supervisor and a wonderful person—she also knew when to close her eyes, like the times when we made fudge! Sister Germaine [D'Arcy] also visited the floors at night and always had a treat in her pocket, usually an apple. Sister Gertrude [Gaertner] had a special feeling for nurses; she knew when we were tired, when we'd had a hard day. Sister Basil [O'Connor] was highly perceptive about patients and I learned much from her."

Sister Antoine Murphy, another nursing student who became a Franciscan, recalled a feeling of family at the hospital: "We all knew each other and worked together for the good of the patients. We were proud of the hospital and aware of the visiting physicians and other guests from all over the world. Helen Keller with her teacher, Annie Sullivan visited Saint Marys. Dr. Claude Dixon invited me to meet Miss Keller. When I went to her room, Annie Sullivan wrote my name for Miss Keller and she called me by name. It was a memorable experience."

To many of the employees of Saint Marys Hospital, the Sisters seemed omnipresent. They were everywhere, and their informal network told them everything that happened in the hospital. By the 1930s, nearly every patient floor or medical area was known by the name of the Sister in charge. One of them was Sister Samuel Reinartz, who began the obstetrics department in 1922. For 29 years, Sister Samuel supervised the department and assisted at some 19,000 deliveries. "Many times," she recalled, "I would say to the parents of a new baby, 'I remember when you were in the nursery.'" Sister Samuel made it a practice to walk every mother to the hospital door when she left to go home.

Sister Frances McManimon.

Sister Samuel's harmonious working relationship with the head of pediatrics, Robert D. Mussey, M.D., was an essential ingredient of good patient care in obstetrics. Indeed, in every department throughout the hospital, a mutual commitment to the best in patient care distinguished the relationship of Mayo Clinic physicians and the Sisters. The Sisters consistently did their best to accommodate physicians' requests. The physicians, in turn, were keenly sensitive that Saint Marys was not their hospital and maintained a respectful but formal relationship with the Sisters. The pervading feeling was that ultimately the hospital belonged to the patients and the physicians and Sisters worked together on their behalf.

Sister Samuel Reinartz. (From Saint Marys School of Nursing Archives.)

Sisters held Doctors William J. (Will) and Charles H. (Charlie) Mayo in deep, affectionate regard, and the Mayos showed them great kindness in countless ways. Inviting the Sisters to enjoy the Mississippi River on their boat was one of them. Sister-guests on the Mayos' paddle-wheel steamer wrote a note of appreciation, shown on the facing page. The Mayos had a great love for the Mississippi River and during their lifetimes owned three riverboats. In 1922, they purchased the gas-engined *North Star* and for many years almost every Sister at Saint Marys Hospital went for a summer outing on it. The hospital annals offers some interesting detail about the 1933 excursion: "September 4-9. The Sisters of Saint Mary's had their annual excursion on the Mississippi as guests of Dr. and Mrs. W. J. Mayo and Dr. and Mrs. C. H. Mayo aboard the *North Star*. Each Sister had one day and night on the river. We went aboard at Wabasha, sailed up to a point on the Wisconsin side not far from Red Wing, where we anchored for the night; next day, we went on up past Red Wing and back to Wabasha where the Doctors' cars met us and brought us home about 5 p.m."

The Mayos strongly supported Saint Marys School of Nursing and made it a regular practice to visit the nursing classes. Dr. Will or Dr. Charlie, sometimes both, officiated at the annual commencement exercises and often hosted an event for the nursing graduates in one of their homes or on the riverboat.

A thank-you note from a group of Sisters to the Mayo brothers after an outing on the paddle-wheel steamer Minnesota. *(From Mayo Magazine. Fall/Winter 1999, p 3. By permission of Mayo Foundation for Medical Education and Research.)*

Sister Domitilla DuRocher excelled as educational director of the School of Nursing. A leader in her field, she received key appointments to state and national committees. For almost 20 years she served on the Minnesota State Board of Examiners of Nurses. In the contentious climate of nursing at the time, the board and its members often became a target of severe criticism. Sister Domitilla must have been gratified in 1931 when the board received a letter of commendation from Dr. Will in support of her efforts. A notation in the minutes reads: "Letter from Dr. Mayo presented, stating his and Dr. Chas. Mayo's appreciation of *Sr. Domitilla's Service* to the nursing profession and to the sick, and their pleasure in doing anything they can to further the work."

Fourteen years after completing her undergraduate degree at Columbia University, Sister Domitilla returned to the university for her Master of Arts degree, in 1934. During this time she helped create an academic program

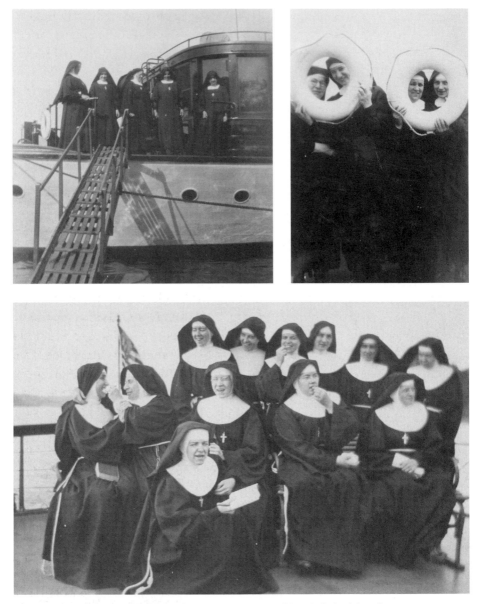

Sisters aboard the North Star. *(From Saint Marys Hospital Archives.)*

leading to a bachelor of science in nursing. Sister Domitilla initiated the program at the College of Saint Teresa in 1935 and became its first director. Saint Marys Hospital provided clinical experience for the college program under the supervision and faculty of the hospital's School of Nursing: "The college program opened new doors for nursing students who planned to further their education . . . and it paid great dividends for the Sisters, many of whom went on to earn their master's degrees . . . at prestigious universities around the country."

"Need, not personal convenience," wrote Sister Mary Brigh Cassidy, "has come first in [Sister Domitilla's] decisions." This observation was clearly evident in 1937 when Sister Domitilla agreed to serve as hospital administrator. Sister Joseph, who was 81 years old, needed to retire, and Sister Domitilla was the logical successor. No doubt Sister Domitilla would have preferred to remain in nursing education; she loved the field personally and was a national leader. However, she believed it was important for the hospital that she serve as administrator and relinquished her chosen profession of nursing education to become the second administrator at Saint Marys Hospital. She assumed the position without specific preparation and, even for one as able as Sister Domitilla, learning hospital administration on the job was a daunting assignment. She was not well known to most Mayo Clinic physicians, notes her biographer, but Sister Domitilla's approach to human relations quickly smoothed out difficulties: "She seemed to have an uncanny skill of knowing when to do or say something. She had something of a politician about her. When she was first administrator, there were a few doctors that she could not please; something was always wrong. She would deliberately put them on committees dealing with the particular problems that they were complaining about."

Sister Domitilla established her authority quickly by taking several initiatives. One of them related to the Saint Marys Hospital Committee, which included members from both the hospital and Mayo Clinic. The large and unwieldy committee did not perform to the satisfaction of either institution. Sister Domitilla created a six-member executive committee and served as chairperson. The executive committee included three physicians: Melvin Henderson, M.D., head of orthopedic surgery; Lee W. Pollack, M.D., head of a section of internal medicine; and Bayard T. Horton, M.D., medical education and research. Sisters Dionysia Mentel and

Sister Domitilla DuRocher. (From Saint Marys Hospital Archives.)

Antonia Rostomily, along with Sister Domitilla, represented Saint Marys Hospital. Minutes for the first meeting on March 18, 1938, gave the executive committee's ground rules: "Meetings are to be called by the chairman when the need arises and at the suggestion of any member. Reports of meetings are to be sent to each member and to the secretary of the large hospital committee."

Interestingly, the first item on the agenda was on parking privileges for the physicians. Sister Domitilla's large volume of letters in the archives underlines her preference for this form of communication. The correspondence, well written and appropriately business-like, occasionally shows another side of the new assistant superintendent. A distraught patient from Willmar, Minnesota, wrote her about the excessive use of radios on the surgical floor and she replied: "Your letter relative to the radio situation at Saint Marys Hospital has been received. I heartily agree with you—a radio is a most damnable thing in a hospital, especially when it is in the hands of a person who has no consideration for his neighbor. We are exceedingly sorry that you had such an unpleasant experience, but we are grateful to you for writing to us about it."

As Sister Domitilla took on new responsibilities, Sister Joseph had no problem setting them aside. She continued to visit patients regularly, as always paying particular attention to the poor, alcoholics, and small children. She also had time to become acquainted with a niece, the daughter of her brother Dennis, who had recently joined the congregation. Sister Carmela Dempsey's first assignment was teaching at Saint John's School in Rochester; she well remembers getting to know her aunt in those years: "My superior, Sister Edith Whelan, urged me to visit Sister Joseph on a regular basis and become better acquainted. I usually went to Saint Marys on Sundays and arrived in time for dinner— the sisters always left a place for me on Sister's right side. After dinner, Sister Joseph liked to take me around the hospital to visit the Sisters. She loved the sisters in domestic work and was a great friend of Sister Hugh [Hondl] in the kitchen and

Sister Carmela Dempsey, Sister Joseph's niece.

Sister Barnabas [Schroeder] in the bakery. They loved her too and told me they could tell her anything—they liked to call her 'Mother Joseph.' Sometimes we went for a ride in the country. Sister Blaise [Roth] drove the seven-passenger Packard the Mayos gave the sisters. She was a wild driver and I was scared to death, but Sister Joseph loved it—she always wanted the front seat to have a better view of the crops. We usually stopped at Saint Mary's Farm where Sister Joseph visited with the men at length about crops and animals and farm machinery."

Sister Carmela and her aunt shared a love for teaching children, and Sister Joseph confided, "When I came to Saint Marys, I missed teaching so much that I cried myself to sleep every night for a year." In one of their visits, Sister Joseph looked at her intently and said, "I suppose you're like me when I came to the convent. I thought I could change the world — but I found out that I couldn't change anyone but myself."

Like Sister Joseph, Doctors Will and Charlie Mayo also anticipated their retirement. As early as 1928, Dr. Will told his secretary, on July 1: "I've just done my last operation." At 67, he wanted to stop "while I'm still good." Dr. Charlie's retirement came unexpectedly a year and a half later when he suffered a retinal hemorrhage. Fortuitously, a decade earlier Dr. Will, who served as administrative head of Mayo Clinic, conceived and implemented a plan that would prepare the institution for the brothers' retirement. Mayo Clinic historian Clark W. Nelson describes the Clinic's new organizational structure: "Initially, the brothers established the Board of Governors, charged with the operation of the Clinic. Shortly thereafter, the Mayos instituted a system of committees responsible for specific areas. . . . Membership on the committees came primarily from the medical staff. Through such committee activities, members learned about Clinic operations and later became candidates for appointment to the Board of Governors."

In 1932, Dr. Will announced that he, Dr. Charlie, and Henry S. Plummer, M.D., would resign from the Board of Governors at the end of the year. They would form an advisory committee and as long as they lived the benefit of their experience would be at the command of the Clinic, but they were resigning the control and the responsibility to others.

With the retirement of Sister Joseph and the Mayos, the relative informality of communication between Saint Marys Hospital and Mayo Clinic changed. It had worked well for them during the years of development. Sister Joseph and the Doctors Mayo made some of their most important decisions sitting around a hospital kitchen table. By the 1930s, however, the

institutions required a different
approach to organization. At the end
of 1938, Mayo Clinic administrator
Harry J. Harwick, a protégé of Dr.
Will, wrote Sister Domitilla: "Our
objective is the same;" Mr. Harwick
emphasized, "namely, to provide
constantly improved care for the
patient." He went on to propose a
plan, a lynchpin of transition, that
served both institutions well. "The
relationship which has existed
between Saint Mary's Hospital and
the Clinic for many years has been
a pleasant one. In the past mutual
problems of hospital and Clinic were
efficiently and satisfactorily solved
as a result of conference between
Sister Mary Joseph and Dr. W. J.

Harry J. Harwick.

Mayo . . . it seems to the Board of Governors that a plan should be developed so that questions arising from time to time which affect both Saint
Mary's Hospital and the Clinic can be discussed and decided in conference."

The year 1939 was a most difficult one for Mayo Clinic with the loss of
both of its founders. Those remarkable brothers, giants in their day and for
all time, died within 2 months of each other. Beloved Dr. Charles H. Mayo,
73 years old, died in Chicago from lobar pneumonia on May 26. When Dr.
Charlie's remains were brought back to Rochester, the funeral procession
passed landmarks in his life, one of them was Saint Marys Hospital, where
hundreds of white-uniformed nurses lined the street in tribute. Revered
Dr. William J. Mayo, 78 years old, died in his sleep in Rochester on July 28.
Again, at Saint Marys Hospital, hundreds of nurses lined the street for the
funeral procession in tribute to Dr. Will.

Biographer Helen Clapesattle closes her book on the Doctors Mayo with
these ringing words: "They may raise shafts of stone and piles of brick to
the memory of William James and Charles Horace Mayo, but so long as
that spirit lasts in the Clinic they created they will have a monument more
fitting, a living memorial in their own image."

Sister Joseph Dempsey also died in 1939, on March 29, of an acute respiratory infection. Her niece, Sister Carmela, then stationed in Wausau, Wisconsin, was called to her bedside before she died. Sister Joseph smiled when she arrived and said, "I missed your visits after you left." In Sister Joseph's last days, Sister Carmela remembers how the Sisters and Father Galligan came to the hospital room whenever they could spare a few minutes: "I marveled at those wonderful, hard-working hospital sisters who came, often still in their aprons, just to sit for awhile and pray with Sister Joseph. This was a very difficult time for Father Galligan—he sobbed so hard that he could barely lead us in the prayers for the dying. She was like a mother to him."

Dignitaries of church and state gave Sister Joseph high praise and recognition, which the press and other publications quoted at length. For this daughter of immigrants, however, the eulogy of a Saint Paul streetcar conductor seems a most fitting tribute: "This morning when I arrived at work they had the morning paper and everyone was discussing the passing of

Saint Marys Hospital, 1939. (From Saint Marys Hospital Archives.)

your grand old Sister Joseph. Swedes, Norwegians, Irish, all the city's melting pot—you would be surprised how many of these rough working-men had met her through sickness, trouble or something else. I saw more than one rough hand wipe away an unconscious tear. On the streetcar I heard passengers speaking of her. She surely served her time to a suffering public and I am sure she will never be forgotten."

The deaths of Doctors Will and Charlie and Sister Joseph in 1939, the hospital's golden anniversary, brings this story to a close. More than 100 Sisters lived and served at Saint Marys Hospital during these years. Unlike Sister Joseph, few of them were known to many beyond the confines of the hospital. However, thousands of patients and others at the hospital would remember how they worked and prayed with one purpose in mind, to serve the good of the patients. Along with Sisters across the country who also served on the American frontier, they followed in the footsteps of women called to a life of service that dated back to the early years of Christianity.

The Sisters' Story of Saint Marys Hospital began like many good stories. Once upon a time, a group of Catholic Sisters and a family of physicians built a hospital in a cornfield. The hospital grew to become a place of healing for people from all over the world. Like other good stories, it concludes, everyone lived happily ever after—if not in this world, most certainly in the next.

ENDNOTES

Page 141   **Saint Marys Hospital Annals, 1927 to 1932.**
            Registration numbers documented.

Page 141   *A Century of Caring: 1889-1989.* **Rochester, MN: Saint Marys Hospital, 1988, p 40.**
            The Sisters' efforts to find employment for nurses.

Page 142   **Saint Marys Hospital Annals, 1933.**
            The sanguine note about new congregational leadership.

            Heritage Task Force: *A Franciscan Symphony of Courage & Creativity.* **Rochester, MN: Mayo Foundation for Medical Education and Research, 1996, p 13.**
            Describes the new mother general.

Page 142   Interview with Sister Bibiana Lewis, May 10, 2001.
            Mother Aquinas' comments about the sheriff at her door. Sister Bibiana also describes the meeting with Bishop Francis Kelly.

Pages 142-143   Taped interview with Sister M. Adele O'Neil, February 29, 1980.
            The story of her financial odyssey.

Page 143   **Saint Marys Hospital Annals, 1932.**
            Sister Joseph Dempsey's note on the chapel fund.

Page 144   **Saint Marys Hospital Annals, 1903.**
            "The design of the chapel was made by Mr. Victor Cordella and executed by Italian artists and artisans who had been employed on the St. Louis Exposition Buildings. All the mural figures were made here."

Pages 145-146   **Saint Marys Hospital Archives, 1932.**

            Saint Marys Hospital Annals, 1933.
            The story of the pipe organ.

Page 146   *What the Chaplain Should Contribute to the Teamwork of the Hospital, June 8, 1916.* **Saint Marys Hospital Annals, 1918.**
            Father Francis Tracy's remarks.

Pages 146-147   *A Century of Caring: 1889-1989,* **p 66.**
            Description of Father Raymond Galligan.

Page 147   Sister Antoine Murphy, O.S.F., recalled Father Galligan's comment
               about his horse in a September 21, 1998, interview.

Page 147   **Saint Marys Hospital Annals, 1933.**
               A note describing Archbishop John Murray's presentation to the
               Minnesota State Medical Association.

               Sister Joseph Dempsey's nieces recalled the archbishop's exchange with
               their aunt, Sister Beatrice Dempsey, in a November 4, 1999, interview.

Pages 147-148 Interview with Sister Regina Buskowiak, O.S.F., September 21, 1998.

Page 149   Interview with Sister Frances McManimon, O.S.F., September 22, 1998.

Page 149   **Saint Marys Hospital Annals, 1939.**

Pages 149-150 *Caring.* **Saint Marys Hospital Publication. Summer 1977, p 15.**

               Interview with Sister Samuel Reinartz, O.S.F.

Page 150   Interview with Sister Antoine Murphy, O.S.F., December 21, 1998.

Pages 150-151 **Beck CS, Dacy MD: Hands Across the Mississippi River.** *Mayo*
               Magazine. **Fall/Winter 1999, pp 3-11.**
               Interesting and visual record of the Mayos, their love for riverboats
               and the Mississippi.

Page 150   **Nelson CW:** *Mayo Roots: Profiling the Origins of Mayo Clinic.*
               Rochester, MN: Mayo Foundation, 1990, p 48.
               Describes the Mayos' riverboats in some detail.

Page 150   **Saint Marys Hospital Annals, 1933.**
               Quotation about the September 4 to 9 excursion.

Page 151   **Dusbabek MH:** *The Contributions of Sister M. Domitilla Du Rocher,*
               O.S.F. to Nursing, 1920-1939. **Unpublished dissertation. Catholic**
               University of America, Washington, DC, 1962, p 52.
               Quotes from the minutes about Dr. William J. Mayo's supportive letter
               regarding Sister Domitilla DuRocher.

Pages 151-153 *A Century of Caring: 1889-1989.* **Rochester, MN: Saint Marys Hospital,**
               1988, p 84.
               Makes note of the new college program.

Page 153   **Cassidy MB, O.S.F.:** *Sister M. Domitilla, O.S.F. The Minnesota Registered Nurse.* **23:83, 1950.**

Page 153   **Dusbabek MH:** *The Contributions of Sister M. Domitilla Du Rocher, O.S.F. to Nursing, 1920-1939.* **Supplement, p 2.**

Pages 153-154   **Saint Marys Hospital Annals, 1938.**
Minutes of the Saint Marys Hospital Executive Committee, March 18, 1938.

Page 154   **Saint Marys Hospital Annals, 1938.**
Correspondence of Sister Domitilla.

Pages 154-155   Sister Carmela Dempsey recalled her visits with Sister Joseph in a series of interviews.

Page 155   **Clapesattle H:** *The Doctors Mayo.* **Minneapolis: The University of Minnesota Press, 1941, p 698.**
Recounts the Mayos' decisions to retire.

Pages 155-156   **Nelson CW:** *Mayo Roots: Profiling the Origins of Mayo Clinic,* **pp 116-117.**

Pages 155-156   **Saint Marys Hospital Annals, 1938.**
Memo of H. J. Harwick to Sister M. Domitilla, December 21, 1938.

Page 156   **Clapesattle (p 712).**

Pages 156-158   **Cassidy MB, O.S.F.:** *In Memoriam.* **Saint Mary's Alumni Quarterly. Spring 1939, pp 10-11.**

INDEX